Glossary and Tables for Statistical Quality Control

Fourth Edition

Also available from ASQ Quality Press:

The Desk Reference of Statistical Quality Methods
Mark L. Crossley

The Quality Improvement Glossary
Don Siebels

Statistical Quality Control Using Excel, Second Edition
Steven M. Zimmerman, PhD and Marjorie L. Icenogle, PhD

Statistical Procedures for Machine and Process Qualification,
Third Edition
Edgar Dietrich and Alfred Schulze

Improving Performance through Statistical Thinking
ASQ Statistics Division

To request a complimentary catalog of ASQ Quality Press publications,
call 800-248-1946, or visit our Web site at http://qualitypress.asq.org.

Glossary and Tables for Statistical Quality Control

Fourth Edition

ASQ Statistics Division

ASQ Quality Press
Milwaukee, Wisconsin

American Society for Quality, Quality Press, Milwaukee 53203
© 2005 by ASQ
All rights reserved. Published 2004
Printed in the United States of America

12 11 10 09 08 07 06 05 04   5 4 3 2 1

Library of Congress Cataloging-in-Publication Data

Glossary and tables for statistical quality control / ASQ Statistics
Division.—4th ed.
   p. cm.
   Includes bibliographical references.
   ISBN 0-87389-631-9 (soft cover, perfect bound : alk. paper)
   1. Quality control—Statistical methods—Terminology. 2. Quality
control—Statistical methods—Tables. I. ASQ Statistics Division.

   TS156.A1G53 2004
   658.4'013—dc22   2004012249

ISBN 0-87389-631-9

Publisher: William A. Tony
Acquisitions Editor: Annemieke Hytinen
Project Editor: Paul O'Mara
Production Administrator: Randall Benson
Special Marketing Representative: Matt Meinholz

ASQ Mission: The American Society for Quality advances individual,
organizational, and community excellence worldwide through learning,
quality improvement, and knowledge exchange.

Attention Bookstores, Wholesalers, Schools, and Corporations: ASQ Quality
Press books, videotapes, audiotapes, and software are available at quantity
discounts with bulk purchases for business, educational, or instructional use.
For information, please contact ASQ Quality Press at 800-248-1946, or write to
ASQ Quality Press, P.O. Box 3005, Milwaukee, WI 53201-3005.

To place orders or to request a free copy of the ASQ Quality Press Publications
Catalog, including ASQ membership information, call 800-248-1946. Visit our
Web site at www.asq.org or http://qualitypress.asq.org.

 Printed on acid-free paper

Quality Press
600 N. Plankinton Avenue
Milwaukee, Wisconsin 53203
Call toll free 800-248-1946
Fax 414-272-1734
www.asq.org
http://qualitypress.asq.org
http://standardsgroup.asq.org
E-mail: authors@asq.org

ASQ
AMERICAN SOCIETY
FOR QUALITY™

Contents

Preface

This book began in 1954 as *Symbols, Definitions and Tables for Industrial Statistics and Quality Control*, an internal manual of the Eastman Kodak Company written by Kodak's Industrial Statistics Committee. This committee included quality giants such as Richard A. Freund, J. Edward Jackson, and Donald A. Wright. Kodak gave the Rochester Institute of Technology permission to reproduce and publish the manual, and we continue to build on this legacy as we strive to continue the advancement of practical statistics with a fourth edition of the manual.

What to keep, what to set aside, and what to alter was a challenge to the fourth edition team. Originally, the manual contained many tables, but because of advances in computer technology most of the tables are no longer needed. Therefore, we kept only the standard tables generally found in current statistics textbooks.

We gratefully thank Minitab for their policy allowing use of Minitab software to make calculations. Because of the ability of Minitab and other software to make the needed calculations, we did not include many of the detailed equations that were in previous editions.

The numerous sources we used for this revision are listed in the references. We frequently rewrote definitions so that a wider audience could grasp the meaning of the technical terms, but the definitions would still be technically correct. The third edition made a bold change in format by alphabetizing the terms rather than grouping them by subject. We expanded this concept by weaving the Glossary of Symbols into the listing of the terms. Rather than have an index, we cross-referenced the terms extensively and added a Control Chart Guide. The team investigated adding Six Sigma terms, but found that the statistical terms involved were already included.

The ASQ Statistics Division gave tremendous encouragement and support to the team. Bob Mitchell, Statistics Division Chair 2002–03, was always available. Annemieke Hytinen, ASQ Quality Press Acquisitions Editor, provided assistance on numerous questions. James Bossert, third edition editor, gave initial support.

The dedicated team members who worked continuously with me were Georgia Kay Carter, Willis Jensen, Herb Monnich, and Glen Page.

Rudy Kittlitz
Editor

Acknowledgments

ASQ and the Statistics Division appreciate the contributions of the authors of this revision. They are:

Georgia Kay Carter

Willis Jensen

Rudolf G. Kittlitz, Jr. (Chair)

Herbert Monnich, Jr.

Glen Page

I

Glossary of Terms

To make this section more user friendly, numbers and symbols have been included in the alphabetization under the following guidelines:

- Numbers precede letters and are not alphabetized by their spelled-out equivalent.

- Greek letters are alphabetized as their closest English equivalent, and precede the English. Example: α precedes a; β precedes b; χ precedes x.

- Subscripts and superscripts are ignored.

Cross-references to other terms are indicated by italics.

1 – α   See *confidence level.*

1 – β   The power of testing a hypothesis is $1 - \beta$. It is the probability of correctly rejecting the *null hypothesis, H_0.*[26]

2^k factorial design   A *factorial design* in which *k factors* are studied, each of them at exactly two *levels.*[19]

100 percent inspection   An inspection of selected *characteristic*(s) of every *item* in the group under consideration.[18]

α (alpha) 1: The maximum probability, or risk, of making a *type I error* when dealing with the *significance level* of a test.
2: The *probability* or risk of incorrectly deciding that a shift in the process mean has occurred when the process is unchanged (when referring to α in general or as the *p-value* obtained in a test).
3: α is usually designated as producer's risk.[12]

Ac See *acceptance number.*

Acceptable process level (APL) The process level that forms the outer boundary of the zone of acceptable processes. (A process located at the APL will have only a *probability of rejection* designated α when the plotted statistical measure is compared to the acceptance control limits.)

Note: In the case of two-sided tolerances, upper and lower acceptable process levels will be designated UAPL and LAPL. (These need not be symmetrical around the standard level.)[4]

Acceptable process zone See *zone of acceptable process.*

Acceptance (control chart or acceptance control chart usage)	A decision that the *process* is operating in a satisfactory manner with respect to the *statistical measure* being plotted.[4]

Acceptance control chart	A *control chart* intended primarily to evaluate whether or not the plotted measure can be expected to satisfy specified *tolerances*.[18]

Acceptance control limit (ACL)	*Control limits* for an *acceptance control chart* that permit some assignable shift in process level based on specified requirements, provided within-*subgroup* variability is in a *state of statistical control*.[18]

Acceptance number (Ac)	The largest number of *nonconformities* or nonconforming items found in the *sample* by *acceptance sampling inspection by attributes* that permits the acceptance of the lot as given in the *acceptance sampling plan*.[18]

Acceptance quality limit (AQL)	The AQL is the *quality* level that is the worst tolerable product average when a continuing series of lots is submitted for *acceptance sampling*.

Note 1: This concept only applies when an *acceptance sampling scheme* with rules for switching and for discontinuation is used.

Note 2: Although individual lots with quality as bad as the acceptance quality limit can be accepted with fairly high probability, the designation of an acceptance quality limit does not suggest that this is a desirable quality level.

Note 3: *Acceptance sampling schemes* found in standards, with their rules for switching and |

for discontinuation of sampling inspection, are designed to encourage suppliers to have process averages consistently better than the acceptance quality limit. If suppliers fail to do so, there is a high probability of being switched from *normal inspection* to *tightened inspection,* where *lot* acceptance becomes more difficult. Once on tightened inspection, unless corrective action is taken to improve product quality, it is very likely that the rule requiring discontinuance of sampling inspection will be invoked.

Note 4: The use of the abbreviation AQL to mean acceptable quality level is no longer recommended since modern thinking is that no fraction defective is really acceptable. Using "acceptance quality limit" rather than "acceptable quality level" indicates a technical value where acceptance occurs.[2, 3]

Acceptance sampling
A sampling after which decisions are made to accept or not to accept a *lot,* or other grouping of product, material, or service, based on sample results.[18]

Acceptance sampling inspection
An acceptance *inspection* where the acceptability is determined by sampling *inspection.*[18]

Acceptance sampling inspection by attributes
An *acceptance sampling inspection* whereby the presence or absence of specified *characteristics* of each item in a sample is observed to statistically establish the acceptability of a *lot* or *process.*[18]

Acceptance sampling inspection by variables
An *acceptance sampling inspection* in which the acceptability of a *process* is determined statistically from measurements on specified

quality *characteristics* of each item in a *sample* from a *lot.*

Note: Lots taken from an acceptable process are assumed to be acceptable.[18]

Acceptance sampling inspection system
A collection of *acceptance sampling plans* or *acceptance sampling schemes* together with criteria by which appropriate plans or schemes may be chosen.[18]

Acceptance sampling plan
A plan that states the *sample size(s)* to be used and the associated criteria for *lot* acceptance.[18]

Acceptance sampling procedure
The operational requirements and/or instructions related to the use of a particular *acceptance sampling plan.*

Note: This covers the planned method of selection, withdrawal, and preparation of *sample(s)* from a *lot* to yield knowledge of the *characteristic*(s) of the lot.[18]

Acceptance sampling scheme
The combination of *acceptance sampling plans* with *switching rules* for changing from one plan to another.[18]

Acceptance sampling system
A collection of sampling schemes.[14]

Accessibility
A measure of the relative ease of admission to the various areas of a piece of equipment for the purpose of operation or maintenance.[24]

Accuracy
The closeness of agreement between a test result or measurement result and the true value.[18]

ACL   See *acceptance control limit.*

Action limits   The *control chart control limits* (for a process *in a state of statistical control*) beyond which there is a very high probability that a value is not due to chance. When a measured value lies beyond an action limit, appropriate corrective action should be taken on the process.

Example: Typical action limits for a $\bar{x}$ *chart* are $\pm 3\,\hat{\sigma}$ (3 *standard deviations*).[18]

Alias   An *effect* that is completely confounded with another effect due to the nature of the designed experiment. Aliases are the results of *confounding,* which may or may not be deliberate.[19]

Alternative hypothesis, H_1   A hypothesis that is accepted if the *null hypothesis* (H_0) is disproved.

Example: Consider the null hypothesis that the statistical model for a *population* is a *normal distribution.* The alternative hypothesis to this null hypothesis is that the statistical model of the population is **not** a normal distribution.

Note 1: The alternative hypothesis is a statement that contradicts the null hypothesis. The corresponding test statistic is used to decide between the null and alternative hypotheses.

Note 2: The alternative hypothesis can be denoted H_1, H_A, or H^A with no clear preference as long as the symbolism parallels the null hypothesis notation.[12, 17]

Analysis of covariance (ANCOVA)   A technique for estimating and testing the effects of treatments when one or more *concomitant variables* influence the *response variable.*

Note: Analysis of covariance can be viewed as a combination of *regression analysis* and *analysis of variance.*[19]

Analysis of variance (ANOVA)   A technique to determine if there are statistically significant differences among group means by analyzing group *variances.* An ANOVA is an analysis technique that evaluates the importance of several factors of a set of data by subdividing the variation into component parts. An analysis of variance table generally contains columns for:

- Source

- *Degrees of freedom*

- Sum of squares

- Mean square

- *F*-ratio or *F-test* statistic

- *p-value*

- Expected mean square

The basic assumptions are that the *effects* from the sources of *variation* are additive and that the *experimental errors* are independent, normally distributed, and have equal *variances.* ANOVA tests the *hypothesis* that the within-group variation is homogeneous and does not vary from group to group. The *null hypothesis* is that the group means are equal to each other. The *alternative hypothesis* is that at least one of the group means is different from the others.[19]

ANCOVA   See *analysis of covariance.*

ANOVA   See *analysis of variance.*

AOQ   See *average outgoing quality.*

AOQL   See *average outgoing quality limit.*

APL   See *acceptable process level.*

AQL   See *acceptance quality limit.*

Arithmetic average   See *arithmetic mean.*

Arithmetic mean   A calculation or estimation of the center of a set of values. It is a sum of the values divided by the number in the sum.

$$\bar{x} = \frac{1}{n}\sum_{i=1}^{n} x_i$$

where $\bar{x}$ is the arithmetic mean.

The average of a set of n observed values is the sum of the observed values divided by n:

$$\bar{x} = \frac{x_1 + x_2 + \ldots + x_n}{n} \ .$$

See also *sample mean* and *population mean.*[8, 17]

ARL (average run length)   See *average run length.*

ASN   See *average sample number.*

Assignable cause   A specifically identified factor that contributes to *variation* and is feasible to detect and identify. Eliminating assignable causes so that the points plotted on a *control chart* remain within the *control limits* helps achieve a *state of statistical control.*

Note: Although assignable cause is sometimes considered synonymous with *special cause,* a special cause is assignable only when it is specifically identified.[18]

ATI   See *average total inspection.*

Attribute   A countable or categorized quality *characteristic* that is *qualitative* rather than *quantitative* in nature. Attribute data come from *discrete, nominal,* or *ordinal scales.* Examples of attribute data are irregularities or flaws in a sample and results of pass/fail tests.[12, 18]

Attribute control chart   A *Shewhart control chart* where the measure plotted represents countable or categorized data.[18]

Attributes, inspection by   See *inspection by attributes.*

Autocorrelation   The internal *correlation* between members of a series of observations ordered in time.

Example: Test values taken from hourly samples of a tank to which material is being continuously added. Each value represents material already in the tank plus the new material and contains material that was part of the previous sample.

Note: Autocorrelation can lead to misinterpretation of *runs* and trends in *control charts.*[18]

A

Availability The *probability* that a system or equipment is operating satisfactorily at any point in time when used under stated conditions. The total time considered includes operating time, active repair time, administrative time, and logistic time.[33]

Average The central tendency. Common measures are the *mean, median,* or *mode* and the calculation depends on the type of distribution. If the term *average* is used without any descriptor, it is ordinarily the *arithmetic mean.*[30]

Average outgoing quality (AOQ) The expected average quality level of outgoing product for a given value of incoming product quality.

Note: Unless otherwise specified, the average outgoing quality (AOQ) is calculated over all accepted *lots* plus all nonaccepted lots after the latter have been 100% inspected and the nonconforming items replaced by conforming items. An approximation often used is AOQ equals incoming *process* quality multiplied by the *probability of acceptance.* This formula is exact for accept-zero plans and overestimates other plans.[18]

Average outgoing quality limit (AOQL) The maximum *average outgoing quality* over all possible values of incoming product quality level for a given *acceptance sampling plan* and rectification of all nonaccepted *lots* unless specified otherwise.[18]

Average run length (ARL) The expected number of samples (or *subgroups*) plotted on a *control chart* up to and including the decision point that a *special cause* is present. The choice of ARL is a compromise between taking action when the process has not changed (ARL too small) or not taking action when a special cause is present (ARL too large).[18]

Average sample number (ASN) The average number of sample *units* per *lot* used for making decisions (acceptance or nonacceptance).[4]

Average total inspection (ATI) The average number of items inspected per lot including *100% inspection* of items in nonaccepted *lots.*

Note: Applicable when the procedure calls for 100% inspection of nonaccepted lots.[18]

Axial point See *star point.*

B

β (beta)
1. The maximum *probability,* or risk, of making a *type II error.* See comment on α *(alpha).*
2. The probability or risk of incorrectly deciding that a shift in the *process mean* has not occurred when the process has changed.
3. β is usually designated as *consumer's risk.* See *power curve.*[4]

Balanced design
A design where all *treatment* combinations have the same number of observations. If *replication* in a design exists, it would be balanced only if the replication was consistent across all the treatment combinations. In other words, the number of replicates of each treatment combination is the same.[28]

Balanced incomplete block (BIB) design
An *incomplete block design* in which each *block* contains the same number (k) of different *levels* from the (l) *levels* of the principal *factor* arranged so that every pair of *levels* occurs in the same number (l) of *blocks* from the b *blocks.*

Note: This design implies that every *level* of the principal *factor* appears the same number of times in the experiment.[12, 19]

Batch A definite quantity of product accumulated under conditions considered uniform or accumulated from a common source. This term is sometimes synonymous with *lot.*[13]

Bias Inaccuracy in a *measurement system* that occurs when the *mean* of the measurement result is consistently or systematically different than its *true value.*[30]

BIBD See *balanced incomplete block design.*

Bimodal A probability distribution having two distinct statistical modes.[30]

Binomial confidence interval (one sample) To construct $100(1 - \alpha)\%$ *confidence intervals* on the parameter p of a binomial distribution, if n is large and $p \geq 0.1$. For instance:

$$\hat{p} - z_{\alpha/2}\sqrt{\frac{\hat{p}(1-\hat{p})}{n}} \leq p \leq \hat{p} + z_{\alpha/2}\sqrt{\frac{\hat{p}(1-\hat{p})}{n}}$$

where the unbiased point estimator of p is

$$\hat{p} = x / n.$$

If n is small, then tables of the *binomial distribution* should be used to establish the confidence interval on p. If n is large but p is small, then the Poisson approximation to the binomial is useful in constructing confidence intervals.[26]

Binomial confidence interval (two sample) If there are two binomial parameters of interest, p_1 and p_2, then an approximate $100(1 - \alpha)\%$ *confidence interval on the difference is*

$$\hat{p}_1 - \hat{p}_2 - z_{\alpha/2}\sqrt{\frac{\hat{p}_1(1-\hat{p}_1)}{n_1} + \frac{\hat{p}_2(1-\hat{p}_2)}{n_2}}$$

$$\leq p_1 - p_2 \leq$$

$$\hat{p}_1 - \hat{p}_2 + z_{\alpha/2}\sqrt{\frac{\hat{p}_1(1-\hat{p}_1)}{n_1} + \frac{\hat{p}_2(1-\hat{p}_2)}{n_2}}$$

where $\hat{p}_1 = x_1/n_1$ and $\hat{p}_2 = x_2/n_2$.[26]

B

Binomial distribution A two-parameter discrete distribution involving the *mean, μ,* and the *variance, σ^2,* of the variable x with *probability p* where p is a constant, $0 \leq p \leq 1$, and sample size n. Mean = np and variance = $np(1 - p)$.[30]

Blemish An *imperfection* that causes awareness but does not impair function or usage.[4]

Block A collection of *experimental units* more homogeneous than the full set of experimental units. Blocks are usually selected to allow for *special causes,* in addition to those introduced as *factors* to be studied. These special causes may be avoidable within blocks, thus providing a more homogeneous experimental subspace.[12, 19]

Block effect An *effect* resulting from a *block* in an *experimental design.* Existence of a block effect generally means that the method of blocking was appropriate.[30]

Blocking   The method of including *blocks* in an experiment in order to broaden the applicability of the conclusions or to minimize the impact of selected *assignable causes.* The randomization of the experiment is restricted and occurs within blocks.[30]

Box-Behnken design   A type of *response surface design* constructed by judicious combination of 2^k *factorial designs* with *balanced incomplete block designs.* It is most useful when it is difficult to have more than three *levels* of a *factor* in an experiment or when trying to avoid extreme combinations of *factor levels.*[19]

Boxplot   Boxplots, which are also called box-and-whisker plots, are particularly useful for showing the distributional characteristics of data. A boxplot consists of a box, whiskers, and *outliers.* A line is drawn across the box at the *median.* By default, the bottom of the box is at the *first quartile* (Q1) and the top is at the *third quartile* (Q3) value. The whiskers are the lines that extend from the top and bottom of the box to the adjacent values. The adjacent values are the lowest and highest observations that are still inside the region defined by the following limits:

Lower limit: Q1 – 1.5 (Q3 – Q1)

Upper limit: Q3 + 1.5 (Q3 – Q1)

Outliers are points outside of the lower and upper limits and usually are plotted with asterisks (*).[20, 25, 31, 32]

Sample Boxplot

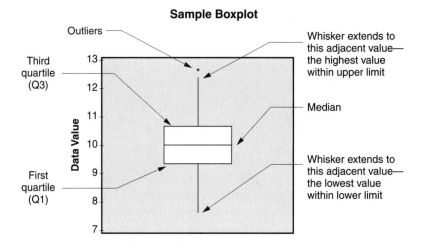

C

c (count)   The number of *events* (often *nonconformities*) of a given classification occurring in a *sample* of fixed size. A *nonconforming unit* may have more than one nonconformity.

Example: *Blemishes* per 100 meters of rubber hose. Counts are *attribute* data. See *c chart*.[4]

Capability   The performance of a *process* demonstrated to be in a *state of statistical control*. See *process capability* and *process performance*.[30]

Capability index   See *process capability index*.

Cause   A cause is an identified reason for the presence of a symptom, *defect,* or problem. See *effect* and *cause-and-effect diagram*.[1]

Cause-and-effect diagram   A basic tool for analyzing a *process;* also called Ishikawa diagram or fishbone diagram. The diagram illustrates the main *causes* and subcauses leading to an *effect*.[1]

CCD   See *central composite design*.

***c* chart (count chart)**
See Part II—Control
Chart Guide

An *attribute control chart* that uses *c (count)* or number of *events* as the plotted values where the opportunity for occurrence is fixed. Events, often *nonconformities,* of a particular type form the count. The fixed opportunity relates to samples of constant size or a fixed amount of material. Examples include flaws in each 100 square meters of fabric; errors in each 100 invoices; number of absentees per month.

Central line: $\bar{c}$

Control limits: $\bar{c} \pm 3\sqrt{\bar{c}}$

where $\bar{c}$ is the *arithmetic mean* of the number of events.

Note: If the *lower control limit* calculates ≤ 0, there is no lower control limit.

See also *u chart,* a count chart where the opportunity for occurrence is variable.[4, 18]

Center line   See *central line.*

Center point   The *experimental runs* in a *factorial design* located at the center of the *design space.* In other words, all the *factor levels* are chosen to be halfway between the high and low settings. Center points can be used to test for *curvature* in the *response variable.* The center points can also be used to get an estimate of *standard deviation* or to test the significance of other *effects* where *replication* does not exist.[19]

Central composite design (CCD)   A type of *response surface design* that includes *center points, cube points,* and *star points.* The design is particularly useful when done sequentially—with the cube points and center points done to check for *curvature* and the star points added if curvature is present.[19]

Central line A line on a *control chart* representing the long-term *average* or a standard value of the *statistical measure* plotted. The central line calculation for each type of *control chart* is given under the specific control chart term; that is, for the *individuals control chart,* the central line is $\bar{x}$.[4]

Chain acceptance sampling inspection An *acceptance sampling inspection* in which the criteria for acceptance of the current *lot* are governed by the sampling results of that *lot* and those of a specified number of the preceding consecutive lots.[18]

Chance cause See *random cause.*

Chance variation See *random cause.*

Characteristic A distinguishing feature or inherent property of a product, *process,* or system related to a requirement. A property that helps to differentiate among items of a given *sample* or *population.* The differentiation may be either *quantitative* (by *variable*) or *qualitative* (by *attribute*).[9, 13, 18]

Checklist A quality tool that is used for processes where there is a large human element. Examples include audit checklists and an airplane pilot's preflight checklist. Checklists serve as reminders and, depending on design, evidence that important items have been observed. A well-designed checklist helps gather information to support findings and observations and serves as a guide and a place to record information.[30]

Chi-square distribution See χ^2 *distribution.*

Chi-square statistic (χ²)   See χ^2.

Chi-square test   See χ^2 *square test.*

Clearance number   As associated with a *continuous sampling plan,* the number of successively inspected units of product that must be found acceptable during the *100 percent inspection* sequence before action to change the amount of inspection can be taken. The clearance number is often designated as i.[5]

Coefficient of determination (R²)   A measure of the part of the *variance* for one *variable* that can be explained by its linear relationship with another variable (or variables). The coefficient of determination is the square of the correlation between the observed *y* values and the fitted *y* values, and is also the fraction of the variation in *y* that is explained by the fitted equation. It is a percentage between zero and 100 with higher values indicating a stronger degree of the combined linear relationship of several predictor variables $x_1, x_2, \ldots x_p$ to the *response variable Y.* See *regression analysis.*[14, 29]

Coefficient of variation (CV)   This measures relative dispersion. It is the *standard deviation* divided by the *mean* and is commonly reported as a percentage.[14]

Common cause   See *random cause.*

Complete block   A *block* that accommodates a complete set of *treatment* combinations.[30]

Completely randomized design	A design in which the *treatments* are assigned at random to the full set of *experimental units*. No *blocks* are involved in a *completely randomized design.*[19]
Completely randomized factorial design	A *factorial design* in which all the *treatments* are assigned at random to the full set of *experimental units*. See *completely randomized design.*[19]
Concomitant variable	A *variable* or *factor* that cannot be accounted for in the data analysis or design of an experiment but whose *effect* on the results should be accounted for. For example, the *experimental units* may differ in the amount of some chemical constituent present in each unit, which can be measured, but not adjusted. See *analysis of covariance.*[19]
Confidence coefficient (1 – α)	See *confidence level.*
Confidence interval	A confidence interval is an estimate of the interval between two *statistics* that includes the *true value* of the *parameter* with some probability. This probability is called the *confidence level* of the estimate. Confidence levels typically used are 90 percent, 95 percent, and 99 percent. The interval either contains the parameter or it does not. See *z-confidence interval, t-confidence interval.*[26]
Confidence level (confidence coefficient) (1 – α)	1. The *probability* that the *confidence interval* described by a set of *confidence limits* actually includes the population parameter.

2. The probability that an interval about a sample *statistic* actually includes the population parameter.[12]

Confidence limits   The endpoints of the interval about the sample *statistic* that is believed, with a specified *confidence level,* to include the population parameter. See *confidence interval.*[14]

Confounding   Indistinguishably combining an *effect* with other effects or *blocks.* When done deliberately, higher-order effects are systematically *aliased* so as to allow estimation of lower-order effects. Sometimes, confounding results from inadvertent changes to a design during the running of an experiment or poor planning of the design. This can diminish or even invalidate the effectiveness of the experiment.[19]

Consistency   See *precision.*

Consumer's risk (β)   The *probability of acceptance* when the quality level has a value stated by the *acceptance sampling plan* as unsatisfactory.

Note 1: Such acceptance is a *type II error.*

Note 2: Consumer's risk is usually designated as *β (beta).*[18]

Continuous distribution   A distribution where data is from a *continuous scale.* Examples of continuous scales include the *normal, t,* and *F* distributions.[30]

Continuous sampling plan   An *acceptance sampling inspection* applicable to a continuous flow process, which involves acceptance or nonacceptance on an item-by-item basis and uses alternative periods of *100 percent inspection* and sampling, depending on the quality of the observed process output.[18]

Continuous scale A scale with a continuum of possible values.

Note: A continuous scale can be transformed into a *discrete scale* by grouping values, but this leads to some loss of information.[18]

Contrast Linear function of the *response values* for which the sum of the coefficients is zero with not all coefficients equal to zero. Questions of logical interest from an experiment may be expressed as contrasts with carefully selected coefficients.[12, 19]

Contrast analysis A technique for estimating the *parameters* of a *model* and making *hypothesis* tests on preselected linear combinations of the *treatments* or *contrasts.*[19]

Control chart
See Part II—Control Chart Guide
A chart that plots a *statistical measure* of a series of *samples* in a particular order to steer the *process* regarding that measure and to control and reduce variation.

Note 1: The order is usually time- or sample number order–based.

Note 2: The control chart operates most effectively when the measure is a process *characteristic* correlated with an ultimate product or service characteristic.[18]

Control chart, acceptance See *acceptance control chart.*

Control chart factor
See Part II—Control
Chart Guide

A factor, usually varying with *sample size,* that converts specified statistics or parameters into *control limits* or a *central line* value.

Note: Common control chart factors for *Shewhart control charts* are d_2, A_2, D_3, and D_4. See Table 5 for control chart factors. See $\bar{x}$ *chart* and *range*.[4]

**Control chart,
standard given**

A *control chart* whose *control limits* are based on adopted standard values applicable to the *statistical measures* plotted on the chart.

Note 1: Standard values are adopted at any time for computing the control limits to be used as criteria for action in the immediate future or until additional evidence indicates need for revision.

Note 2: This type of control chart is used to discover whether *observed values* differ from standard values by an amount greater than chance. An example of this use is to establish and verify an *internal reference material.*

Note 3: The subscript zero is used for standard chart parameters, that is, $\bar{x}_0$, $\bar{y}_0$, R_0.[8, 12, 30]

Control factor

In *robust parameter design,* a *control factor* is a *predictor variable* that is controlled as part of the standard experimental conditions. In general, inference is made on control factors while *noise factors* are allowed to vary to broaden the conclusions.[30]

Control limit

A line on a *control chart* used for judging the stability of a *process.*

Note 1: Control limits provide statistically determined boundaries for the *deviations* from the *central line* of the statistic plotted on a *Shewhart control chart* due to *random causes* alone.

Note 2: Control limits (with the exception of the *acceptance control chart*) are based on actual process data, not on *specification limits.*

Note 3: Other than points outside of *control limits*, out-of-control criteria can include *runs, trends, cycles, periodicity,* and unusual patterns within the control limits.

Note 4: The control limit calculation for each type of control chart is given under the specific control chart term; that is, for the *individuals control chart* under calculation of its control limits.[18]

Control plan   A document describing the system elements to be applied to control *variation* of *processes,* products, and services in order to minimize deviation from their preferred values.[18]

Corner point   See *cube point.*

Correlation   Correlation measures the linear association between two variables. It is commonly measured by the *correlation coefficient, r.* See also *regression.*[30]

Correlation coefficient (r)   A number between −1 and 1 that indicates the degree of linear relationship between two sets of numbers.

$$r = \frac{s_{xy}}{s_x s_y} = \frac{n\sum xy - \sum y}{\sqrt{\left[n\sum x^2 - \left(\sum x\right)^2 - \left(\sum y\right)^2\right]}}$$

where s_x is the *standard deviation* of x, s_y is *standard deviation* of y, and s_{xy} is the *covariance* of x and y.

Correlation coefficients of –1 and +1 represent perfect linear agreement between two variables; $r = 0$ implies no linear relationship at all. If r is positive, y increases as x increases. In other words, if a *linear regression equation* were fit, the *linear regression coefficient* would be positive. If r is negative, y decreases as x increases. In other words, if a linear regression equation were fit, the linear regression coefficient would be negative.[14]

Covariance   This measures the relationship between pairs of observations from two variables. It is the sum of products of *deviations* of pairs of variables in a random *sample* from their sample means divided by the number in the sum minus one.

$$\text{Sample covariance} = \frac{1}{n-1}\sum_{i=1}^{n}\left(x_i - \bar{x}\right)\left(y_i - \bar{y}\right)$$

where $\bar{x}$ is the sample *mean* for the first sample and $\bar{y}$ is the sample mean for the second sample.

Note: Using $n - 1$ provides an unbiased estimator of the *population* covariance.

When the covariance is standardized to cover a range of values from –1 to 1, it is more commonly known as the *correlation coefficient*.[14, 17]

Cp (process capability index)   An index describing *process capability* in relation to specified *tolerance* of a *characteristic* divided by a measure of the length of the *reference interval* for a process in a *state of statistical control*.

$$Cp = \frac{U - L}{6\sigma}$$

where U is upper specification limit, L is lower *specification limit,* and 6σ is the process capability.

See also *Pp,* a similar term, except that the *process* may not be in a *state of statistical control.*[18, 23]

Cpk (minimum process capability index)

An index that represents the smaller of Cpk_U *(upper process capability index)* and Cpk_L *(lower process capability index).*[18]

Cpk$_L$ (lower process capability index; CPL)

An index describing *process capability* in relation to the lower *specification limit.*

$$Cpk_L = \frac{\mu - L}{3\sigma}$$

where μ = process average, L = lower specification limit, and 3σ = half of the *process capability.*[11, 18]

Cpk$_U$ (upper process capability index; CPU)

An index describing *process capability* in relation to the upper *specification limit.*

$$Cpk_U = \frac{U - \mu}{3\sigma}$$

where μ = process average, U = upper specification limit, and 3σ = half of the *process capability.*[11, 18]

Cpm (process capability index of the mean)

An index that takes into account the location of the mean, defined as

$$Cpm = \frac{(U - L)/2}{3\sqrt{\sigma^2 + (\mu - T)^2}}$$

where U = upper *specification limit*, L = lower specification limit, σ = *standard deviation*, μ = expected value, and T = *target value*.[23]

Critical to quality (CTQ)   A *characteristic* of a product or service that is essential to ensure customer satisfaction.[30]

Crossed design   A design where all the *factors* are crossed with each other. See *crossed factor*.[29]

Crossed factor   Two *factors* are crossed if every *level* of one factor occurs with every level of the other in an experiment.[28]

CTQ   See *critical to quality*.

Cube point   In a design, *experimental runs* that are in the corners of the *design space*. In general, a *factorial design* only consists of corners. They also exist in *fractional factorial designs* and some *central composite designs*.[30]

Cumulative frequency distribution   The sum of the frequencies accumulated up to the upper boundary of a class in a distribution.[16]

Cumulative sum chart (CUSUM chart)
See Part II—Control Chart Guide   The CUSUM *control chart* calculates the cumulative sum of *deviations* from *target* to detect shifts in the level of the measurement. The CUSUM chart can be graphical or numerical. In the graphical form, a V-mask indicates action: whenever the CUSUM trace moves outside the V-mask, take control action. The numerical (or electronic) form computes

CUSUM from a selected bias away from target value and has a fixed *action limit.* Additional tests for abnormal patterns are not required.[11]

Curtailed inspection   An *acceptance sampling procedure* that contains a provision for stopping inspection when it becomes apparent that adequate data have been collected for a decision.[18]

Curvature   The departure from a straight line relationship between the *response variable* and *predictor variable.* Curvature has meaning with *quantitative* predictor variables, but not with *categorical* (nominal) or *qualitative* (ordinal) predictor variables. Detection of curvature requires more than two *levels* of the *factors* and is often done using *center points.*[19]

CUSUM chart   See *cumulative sum chart.*

CV   See *coefficient of variation.*

D

δ (delta lowercase)   The smallest shift in *process* level that it is desired to detect, stated in terms of the number of *standard deviations* from the *average*. It is given by

$$(\delta = D / \sigma)$$

where D is the size of the shift it is desired to detect and σ is the standard deviation.[12]

Δ (delta uppercase)   See *designated imperfection*.

D   The smallest shift in *process* level that it is desired to detect, stated in terms of original units. See *δ (delta)*.[12]

Defect   The nonfulfillment of a requirement related to an intended or specified use.

Note: The distinction between the concepts *defect* and *nonconformity* is important as it has legal connotations, particularly those associated with product liability issues. Consequently, the term *defect* should be used with extreme caution.[2, 18]

Defective (defective unit)	A *unit* with one or more *defects*.[18]
Defects per million opportunities (DPMO)	The measure of capability for *discrete (attribute)* data found by dividing the number of *defects* by the opportunities for defects times a million. It allows for comparison of different types of product.[30]
Defects per unit (DPU)	The measure of capability for *discrete (attribute)* data found by dividing the number of *defects* by the number of units.[30]
Defining relation	Used for *fractional factorial designs*. It consists of *generators* that can be used to determine which *effects* are *aliased* with each other.[28]
Degrees of freedom (ν, df)	In general, the number of independent comparisons available to estimate a specific *parameter* that allows entry to certain statistical tables.[14]
Demerit	A weighting assigned to a classification of an *event* or events to provide a means of obtaining a weighted *quality score*.[4]
Dependability	The measure of the degree to which an item is operable and capable of performing its required function at any (random) time during a specified mission profile, given item availability at the start of the mission.[24]

D

D

Dependent variable   See *response variable.*

Design generator   See *generator.*

Design of experiments   The arrangement in which an experimental
(DOE; DOX)   program is to be conducted, including the
selection of *factor* combinations and
their *levels.*

Note: The purpose of designing an experiment
is to provide the most efficient and economical
methods of reaching valid and relevant conclusions from the experiment. The selection of
the design is a function of many considerations, such as the type of questions to be
answered, the applicability of the conclusions,
the homogeneity of *experimental units,* the
randomization scheme, and the cost to run
the experiment. A properly designed experiment will permit simple interpretation of
valid results.[19]

Design resolution   See *resolution.*

Design space   The multidimensional region of possible
treatment combinations formed by the selected
factors and their *levels.*[30]

Designated   A category of *imperfection* that, because of
imperfection (Δ)   the type and/or magnitude or severity, is to be
treated as an *event* for control purposes.[4]

Deviation   The difference between a measurement and
(measurement usage)   its stated value or intended level.[12]

Deviation control
See Part II—Control
Chart Guide

Deviation control involves *process* control where the primary interest is detecting small shifts in the *mean.* Typical *control charts* used for this purpose are *CUSUM, EWMA,* and *Shewhart control charts* with *runs* rules. This type of control is appropriate in advanced stages of a quality improvement process. See *threshold control.*[11]

Discrete distribution

A *probability distribution* where data are from a *discrete scale.* Examples of *discrete distributions* are *binomial* and *Poisson* distributions. *Attribute* data involve discrete distributions.[17]

Discrete scale

A scale with only a set or sequence of distinct values.

Examples: Defects per unit, events in a given time period, types of defects, number of orders on a truck.[18]

Discrimination

See *resolution.*

Dispersion

A term synonymous with *variation.*[30]

Dispersion effect

The influence of a single *factor* on the *variance* of the *response variable.*[19]

DOE

See *design of experiments.*

Dot plot

A plot of a *frequency distribution* where the values are plotted on the x-axis. The y-axis is a count. Each time a value occurs, the point is plotted according to the count for the value.[30]

Double sampling   A multiple *acceptance sampling inspection* in which, at most, two *samples* are taken.

Note: The decisions are made according to defined rules.[18]

DOX   See *design of experiments.*

Duplication   See *repeated measures.*

Durability   A measure of useful life.[24]

E

EDA   See *exploratory data analysis.*

Effect   The result of taking an action; the expected or predicted impact when an action is to be taken or is proposed. An effect is the symptom, *defect,* or problem. See *cause* and *cause-and-effect diagram.*[1]

Effect (design of experiments usage)   A relationship between a *factor*(s) and a *response variable*(s). Specific types include *main effect, dispersion effect,* or *interaction effect.*[30]

Element   See *unit.*

Event   An occurrence of some *attribute* or outcome. In the quality field, events are often *nonconformities.*[4]

Evolutionary operation (EVOP)   A sequential form of experimentation conducted in production facilities during regular production. The range of variation of the *factor* levels is usually quite small in order to avoid extreme changes, so it often requires considerable *replication* and time. It is most useful when it would be difficult to do standard experimentation techniques like *factorial design.*[19]

EVOP See *evolutionary operation.*

EWMA See *exponentially weighted moving average.*

EWMA chart See *exponentially weighted moving average chart.*

Experiment space See *design space.*

Experimental design See *design of experiments.*

Experimental error The variation in the *response variable* beyond that accounted for by the *factors, blocks,* or other assignable sources in the conduct of an experiment.[19]

Experimental plan The assignment of *treatments* to an *experimental unit* and the time order in which the *treatments* are to be applied.[19]

Experimental run A single performance of an experiment for a specific set of *treatment* combinations.[30]

Experimental unit The smallest entity receiving a particular *treatment,* subsequently yielding a value of the *response variable.*[19]

Experimentation See *design of experiments.*

Explanatory variable See *predictor variable.*

Exploratory data analysis (EDA)

Exploratory data analysis isolates patterns and features of the data and reveals these forcefully to the analyst.[20, 31, 32]

Exponentially weighted moving average (EWMA)

A *moving average* that is not greatly influenced when a small or large value enters the calculation.

$$w_t = \lambda x_i + (1 - \lambda)w_{t-1}$$

where w_t is the exponentially weighted moving average (EWMA) at the present time t, λ *(lambda)* is a defined or experimentally determined weighting factor, x_i is the observed value at time t, and w_{t-1} is the EWMA at the immediately preceding time interval.[30]

Exponentially weighted moving average chart (EWMA chart)
See Part II—Control Chart Guide

A *control chart* where each new result is averaged with the previous *average* value using an experimentally determined weighting factor, λ. Usually only the averages are plotted and the *range* is omitted. The action *signal* is a single point out of limits. The advantage of the EWMA chart compared to the *MA chart* is that the average does not jump when an extreme value leaves the moving average. The weighting factor, λ, can be determined by either an effective time period or by the method covered in Hunter's article (JQT, 1986). Additional tests are not appropriate because of the high correlation between successive averages.[11, 21]

Control limits: $\overline{X}_0 \pm 3\sigma_{w_t}$

Center line: $\overline{X}_0$

$\boldsymbol{F}_{v1, v2}$ *F-test* statistic. See *F-test.*

$\boldsymbol{F}_{v1, v2, \alpha}$ Critical value for *F-test.* See *F-test.*

Factor   A *predictor variable* that is varied with the intent of assessing its *effect* on a *response variable.*[19]

Factor level   See *level.*

Factorial design   An *experimental design* consisting of all possible *treatments* formed from two or more *factors,* each studied at two or more *levels.* When all combinations are run, the *interaction effects* as well as *main effects* can be estimated. See also 2^k *factorial design.*[19]

Failure   The inability, because of *defect*(s), of an item, product, or service to perform its required functions as needed.[14]

Failure mechanism   The physical, chemical, or mechanical *process* that caused the *defect* or *failure.*[14]

Failure mode The type of *defect* contributing to a *failure*.[14]

Failure rate The number of *failures* per unit time (for equal time intervals).[30]

***F* distribution** A *continuous distribution* that is a useful reference for assessing the ratio of independent *variances*. See *tests of variance*. See Table 3A–3G for the actual values of the distribution.[18]

First quartile (Q_1 or lower quartile) The portion of a distribution where one quarter of the data lies below. See *quartiles*.[30]

Fishbone diagram See *cause-and-effect diagram*.

Fixed factor A *factor* that only has a limited number of *levels* that are of interest. In general, inference is not made to other levels of fixed factors not included in the experiment. For example, gender when used as a *factor* only has two possible *levels* of interest. See also *random factor*.[28, 30]

Fixed model A *model* that contains only *fixed factors*.[30]

Flowchart A basic quality tool that uses graphical representation for the steps in a *process*. Effective flowcharts include decisions, inputs, and outputs as well as process steps.[1]

Fractional factorial design An *experimental design* consisting of a subset (fraction) of the *factorial design*. Typically, the fraction is a simple proportion of the full set of possible *treatment* combinations. For example, half-fractions, quarter-fractions, and so forth are common. While fractional factorial designs require fewer runs, some degree of *confounding* occurs.[19]

Frequency   The number of occurrences or *observed values* in a specified class, *sample,* or *population.*[17]

Frequency distribution   A set of all the various values that individual observations may have and the *frequency* of their occurrence in the *sample* or *population.* See *cumulative frequency distribution.*[12]

F-test   A statistical test that uses the *F distribution.* It is most often used when dealing with a *hypothesis* related to the ratio of independent *variances.*

$$F = \frac{s_L^2}{s_S^2}$$

where s_L^2 is the larger variance and s_S^2 is the smaller variance.

See *analysis of variance.* See Tables 3A–3G.[17, 30]

Fully nested design   See *nested design.*

Gage R&R study   A type of *measurement system analysis* done to evaluate the performance of a test method or *measurement system.* Such a study quantifies the capabilities and limitations of a measurement instrument, often estimating its *repeatability* and *reproducibility.* It typically involves multiple operators measuring a series of measurement items multiple times.[28, 30]

Gaussian distribution   See *normal distribution.*

g chart   An *attribute control chart* based on a shifted
See Part II—Control   *geometric distribution* for the number of
Chart Guide   occurrences of a given *event* per *unit* of *process* output. The g chart is for the total number of events.

Center line (CL): $\bar{t}$

Upper control limit (UCL):

$$\bar{t} + k\sqrt{n\left(\frac{\bar{t}}{n} - \alpha\right)\left(\frac{\bar{t}}{n} - \alpha + 1\right)}$$

Lower control limit (LCL):

$$\bar{t} - k\sqrt{n\left(\frac{\bar{t}}{n} - \alpha\right)\left(\frac{\bar{t}}{n} - \alpha + 1\right)}$$

where a is the known minimum possible number of events, n is the *sample size*, k is the σ multiplier (for example, 3σ), and $\bar{t}$ is the average total number of events per *subgroup*. Calculation for $\bar{t}$:

$$\bar{t} = \frac{t_1 + t_2 + ... + t_r}{r}$$

where $t_1 + t_2 + \ldots t_r$ is the total number of events occurring in each subgroup and r is the number of subgroups. (Note that r is not the correlation coefficient r used elsewhere in this glossary.) The g chart is commonly used in healthcare and hospital settings. See *h chart* for the average number of events chart.[22]

Geometric distribution A case of the *negative binomial distribution* where $c = 1$ (c is integer parameter). The geometric distribution is a *discrete distribution*.[17]

Generator In *design of experiments*, a generator is used to determine the level of *confounding* and the pattern of *aliases* in a *fractional factorial design*.[30]

Grade An indicator of category or *rank* related to features or *characteristics* that cover different sets of needs for products or services intended for the same functional use.

Note: Grade reflects a planned difference in requirements or, if not planned, a recognized difference. The emphasis is on functional use and cost relationship.[13]

Graeco-Latin square design An extension of a *Latin square design* that involves four *factors* in which the combination of the *level* of any one of them with the *levels* of the other three appears once and only once.[19]

H₀   See *null hypothesis*.

H₁   See *alternative hypothesis*.

H$_A$ See *alternative hypothesis*.

Hawthorne effect   The *effect* in an experiment that occurs when humans perform better than they normally would because they are being measured or observed.[30]

Hazard rate   See *failure rate*.

h chart
See Part II—Control
Chart Guide   An *attribute control chart* based on a shifted *geometric distribution* for the number of occurrences of a given *event* per unit of *process* output. The h chart is for the *average* number of events.

Center line (CL): $\dfrac{\bar{t}}{n}$.

Upper control limit (UCL):

$$\frac{\bar{t}}{n} + \frac{k}{\sqrt{n}} \sqrt{\left(\frac{\bar{t}}{n} - \alpha\right)\left(\frac{\bar{t}}{n} - \alpha + 1\right)}$$

Lower control limit (LCL):

$$\frac{\bar{t}}{n} - \frac{k}{\sqrt{n}} \sqrt{\left(\frac{\bar{t}}{n} - \alpha\right)\left(\frac{\bar{t}}{n} - \alpha + 1\right)}$$

where a is the known minimum possible number of events, n is the *sample size*, k is the σ multiplier (for example, 3σ), and $\bar{t}$ is the average total number of events per *subgroup*. Calculation for $\bar{t}$:

$$\bar{t} = \frac{t_1 + t_2 + \ldots + t_r}{r}$$

where $t_1 + t_2 + \ldots + t_r$ is the total number of events occurring in each subgroup and r is the number of subgroups. (Note that r is not the correlation coefficient r used elsewhere in this glossary.) The h chart is commonly used in healthcare and hospital settings. See *g chart* for the total number of events chart.[22]

Hierarchical design　See *nested design.*

Histogram　A plot of a *frequency distribution* in the form of rectangles (cells) whose bases are equal to the class interval and whose areas are proportional to the frequencies.[14]

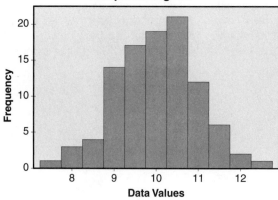

Sample Histogram

Hotelling's T^2   See T^2.

Hypothesis   A statement about a *population* to be tested. See *null hypothesis, alternative hypothesis,* and *hypothesis testing.*[17]

Hypothesis testing   A statistical *hypothesis* is a conjecture about a *population parameter.* There are two statistical hypotheses for each situation—the *null hypothesis (H_0)* and the *alternative hypothesis (H_1)*. The null hypothesis proposes that there is no difference between the population of the sample and the specified population; the alternative hypothesis proposes that there is a difference between the sample and the specified population.[16]

I

i   See *moving average.*

I chart (individuals control chart)   See *individuals control chart.*

Imperfection   The departure of a *characteristic* from its preferred state that may or may not be considered acceptable depending on an interpretation of particular customer needs and expectations.

Note: Imperfection is a general classification. Each imperfection type is usually identified by its specific name (for example, minor scratch or *blemish*).[18]

Imprecision   A measure of *precision* computed as a *standard deviation* of the test or measurement results. Less precision is reflected by a larger standard deviation.[18]

Incomplete block   A *block* that accommodates only a subset of *treatment* combinations. See *balanced incomplete block design.*[30]

Incomplete block design   A design in which the *design space* is subdivided into *blocks* in which there are insufficient *experimental units* available to run a complete *replicate* of the experiment.[19]

In-control process A condition where the existence of *special causes* is no longer indicated by a *Shewhart control chart.* It indicates (within limits) a predictable and *stable process,* but it does not indicate that only *random causes* remain; nor does it imply that the distribution of the remaining values is normal (Gaussian).[27]

Independent variable See *predictor variable.*

Indifference quality level The quality level that, in an *acceptance sampling plan,* corresponds to a *probability of acceptance* of 0.5 when a continuing series of *lots* is considered.[18]

Indifference zone The region containing quality levels between the *acceptance quality limit* and the *limiting quality level.*[18]

Individuals control chart (x chart; I chart)
See Part II—Control Chart Guide
See Table 5

A *variables control chart* with individual values plotted in the form of a *Shewhart control chart* for individuals and *subgroup* size $n = 1$.

Note 1: The x chart is widely used in the chemical industry because of cost of testing, test turnaround time, and the time interval between independent samples.

Note 2: This chart is usually accompanied by a *moving range chart,* commonly with $n = 2$.

Note 3: An individuals chart sacrifices the advantages of averaging subgroups (and the assumptions of the *normal distribution* central limit theorem) to minimize *random variation.*

Central line: $\bar{x}$ (x_0 if standard given).

Control limits: $\bar{x} \pm E_2 \overline{MR}$ or $\bar{x} \pm E_3 \bar{s}$

(if standard given, $x_0 \pm 3\sigma_0$)

where $\bar{x}$ is the average of the individual variables

$$\bar{x} = \frac{x_1 + x_2 + \dots + x_n}{n} ,$$

where R is the range, $\bar{s}$ is average sample standard deviation, x_0 is the standard value for the average, and σ_0 is the standard value for the population standard deviation. (Use the formula with $\overline{MR}$ when the sample size is small; the formula with $\bar{s}$ when the sample is larger, generally >10 to 12.)[8, 11, 14, 18]

Inherent process variation   The variation in a *process* when the process is operating in a *state of statistical control*.[18]

Input variable   A variable that can contribute to the variation in a *process*.[19]

Inspection   A conformity evaluation by observation and judgment accompanied as appropriate by measurement, testing, or gauging.[18]

Inspection, 100 percent   See *100 percent inspection*.

Inspection, attributes   See *inspection by attributes*.

Inspection by attributes   An *inspection* noting the presence, or absence, of the *characteristic*(s) in each of the items in the group under consideration and counting how many items do, or do not, possess the *characteristic*(s), or how many such events occur in the *item*, group, or opportunity space.

Note: When *inspection* is performed by simply noting whether the item is nonconforming or not, the inspection is termed inspection for *nonconforming* items. When inspection is performed by noting the number of nonconformities on each *unit,* the inspection is termed inspection for number of nonconformities.[18]

Inspection by variables   An *inspection* measuring the magnitude(s) of the *characteristic*(s) of an item.[3]

Inspection, curtailed   See *curtailed inspection.*

Inspection level   An index of the relative amount of *inspection* of an *acceptance sampling scheme* chosen in advance and relating the *sample size* to the *lot* size.

Note 1: A lower/higher inspection level can be selected if experience shows that a less or more discriminating *operating characteristic curve* will be appropriate.

Note 2: The term should not be confused with severity of sampling, which concerns *switching rules* that operate automatically.[18]

Inspection lot   A collection of similar units or a specific quantity of similar material offered for inspection and subject to a decision with respect to acceptance.[4]

Inspection, normal   See *normal inspection.*

Inspection, rectifying   See *rectifying inspection.*

Inspection, reduced   See *reduced inspection.*

Inspection, tightened   See *tightened inspection.*

Inspection, variables See *inspection by variables.*

Interaction effect The *effect* for which the apparent influence of one *factor* on the *response variable* depends upon one or more other factors. Existence of an *interaction effect* means that the factors cannot be changed independently of each other.[19]

Interaction plot The plot providing the *average* responses at the combinations of *levels* of two distinct *factors.*[19]

Intercept See *regression analysis.*

Internal reference material A reference material that is not traceable to a national body, but is stable (within stated time and storage conditions), homogeneous, and appropriately characterized.[10]

Interquartile range (IQR) The middle 50 percent of the data obtained by $Q_3 - Q_1$.[30]

IQR See interquartile range.

Ishikawa diagram See *cause-and-effect diagram.*

Isolated lot A unique *lot* or one separated from the sequence of *lots* in which it was produced or collected.[18]

Isolated sequence of lots A group of *lots* in succession but not forming part of a large sequence or produced by a continuing *process.*[18]

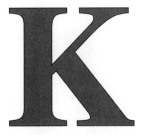

Kurtosis   A measure of peakedness or flattening of a distribution near its center in comparison to the *normal distribution.*[30]

λ (lambda) The weighting factor in *EWMA* calculations where $0 < \lambda \leq 1$.[30]

L See *lower specification limit.*

Latin square design A design involving three *factors* in which the combination of the *levels* of any one of them with the levels of the other two appears once and only once. It is often used to reduce the impact of two blocking factors by balancing out their contributions. A basic assumption is that these block factors do not interact with the factor of interest or with each other. This design is particularly useful when the assumptions are valid for minimizing the amount of experimentation. See *Graeco-Latin square design.*[19]

LCL See *lower control limit.*

Leaf See *stem-and-leaf diagram.*

Least squares, method of A technique of estimating a *parameter* that minimizes the sum of the difference squared, where the difference is between the *observed value* and the predicted value *(residual)* derived from the *model.*

Note: *Experimental errors* associated with individual observations are assumed to be independent. The usual *analysis of variance, regression analysis,* and *analysis of covariance* are all based on the method of least squares.[19]

Level   A potential setting, value, or assignment of a *factor* or the value of the *predictor variable.*[19]

Level of significance   See *significance level.*

Limiting quality level (LQL)   The quality *level* that, for the purposes of *acceptance sampling inspection,* is the limit of an unsatisfactory process average when a continuing series of *lots* is considered.

Note: The limiting quality level is sometimes referred to as the *rejectable quality level* (RQL), *unacceptable quality level* (UQL), or limiting quality (LQ), but limiting quality level (LQL) is the preferred term. When the percentage of *nonconforming units* is expressed as a percent defective, this may be referred to as the *lot tolerance percent defective* (LTPD).[4, 18]

Linear regression coefficients   The values associated with each *predictor variable* in a *linear regression equation.* They tell how the *response variable* changes with each unit increase in the *predictor variable.* See *regression analysis.*[14]

Linear regression equation   A function that indicates the linear relationship between a set of *predictor variables* and a *response variable.* See *regression analysis.*[14]

Linearity (general sense)   The degree to which a pair of variables follow a straight-line relationship. Linearity can be measured by the *correlation coefficient.*[30]

L

Linearity (measurement system sense)
The difference in *bias* through the range of measurement. A measurement system that has good *linearity* will have a constant bias no matter the magnitude of measurement. If one views the relation between the observed measurement result on the y-axis and the *true value* on the x-axis, an ideal *measurement system* would have a line of slope equal to one.[28]

Lognormal distribution
If log x is normally distributed, it is a lognormal distribution. See *normal distribution*.[30]

Lot
A definite part of a population constituted under essentially the same conditions as the *population* with respect to the sampling purpose.

Note: The sampling purpose may, for example, be to determine lot acceptability or to estimate the mean value of a particular *characteristic*.[18]

Lot quality
A *statistical measure* of quality of the product from a given *lot*. These measures may relate to the occurrence of *events* or to physical measurements. For the purposes of this glossary, the most commonly used measure of lot quality is likely to be the percentage or proportion of *nonconforming units* in a *lot*.[4]

Lot size (*N*)
The number of items in a *lot*.[3]

Lot tolerance percent defective (LTPD)
See note under *limiting quality level*.

Lot-by-lot
The *inspection* of a product submitted in a series of *lots*.[18]

L

Lower control limit (LCL) The *control chart* control limit that defines the lower control boundary.[18]

Lower specification limit (lower tolerance limit, L) The *specification* or *tolerance limit* that defines the lower limiting value.[18]

LQL See *limiting quality level.*

LRPL See *rejectable process level.*

LTPD See *lot tolerance percent defective.*

M

μ **(mu)**   See *population mean.*

MA chart   See *moving average chart.*

Main effect   The influence of a single *factor* on the *mean* of a *response variable.*[19]

Main effects plot   A plot giving the *average* responses at the various *levels* of individual *factors.*[19]

Maintainability   The measure of the ability of an item to be retained or restored to specified condition when maintenance is performed by personnel having specified skill levels, using prescribed procedures and resources at each prescribed level of maintenance and repair.[24]

Mean   See *arithmetic mean.*

Mean life   The *arithmetic average* of the lifetimes of all items considered. A lifetime may consist of time between malfunctions, time between repairs, time to removal or replacement of parts, or any other desired interval of observation.[33]

Mean time between failures (MTBF)

The average time between *failure events.* The *mean* number of life units during which all parts of the item perform within their specified limits during a particular measurement interval under stated conditions.[24]

Mean time to failure (MTTF)

The measure of system *reliability* for nonrepairable items is the total number of life units of an item divided by the total number of *failures* within that population during a particular measurement interval under stated conditions. The expectation of the time to failure.[24]

Mean time to repair (MTTR)

The measure of *maintainability* is the sum of corrective maintenance times at any specific level of repair, divided by the total number of *failures* within an item repaired at that *level,* during a particular interval under stated conditions.[24]

Means, tests for

Testing for *means* includes computing a *confidence interval* and hypothesis testing by comparing means to a *population* mean (known or unknown) or to other *sample* means. Which test to use is determined by whether σ is known, whether the test involves one or two samples, and other factors.

If σ is known, the *z-confidence interval* and *z-test* apply.

If σ is unknown, the *t-confidence interval* and *t-test* apply.[26]

Measurement system

Everything that can introduce variability into the measurement *process,* such as equipment, operator, sampling methods, and accuracy.[30]

Measurement systems analysis (MSA)   A statistical analysis of a *measurement system* to determine the variability, *bias, precision,* and *accuracy* of the measurement system(s). Such studies may also include the limit of detection, selectivity, *linearity,* and other *characteristics* of the system in order to determine the suitability of the measurement system for its intended purpose.[10]

Median   The value for which half the *data* is larger and half is smaller. The median provides an estimator that is insensitive to very extreme values in a data set, whereas the *average* is affected by extreme values.

Note: For an odd number of units, the median is the middle measurement; for an even number of units, the median is the average of the two middle measurements.[14, 17]

Meta-analysis   The use of statistical methods to combine the results of multiple studies into a single conclusion.[30]

Method of least squares   See *least squares, method of.*

M_i See *moving average.*

Midrange   (Highest value + lowest value)/2.[30]

Mistake-proofing   The use of *process* or design features to prevent manufacture of nonconforming product.[30]

Mixed variables and attribute sampling   The *inspection* of a sample by *attributes,* in addition to *inspection by variables* already made of a previous *sample* from the *lot,* before a decision as to acceptability or rejectability of the lot can be made.[3]

Mixed model A model where some *factors* are fixed, but other *factors* are random. See *fixed factors* and *random factors.*[19]

Mixture design A design constructed to handle the situation in which the *predictor variables* are constrained to sum to a fixed quantity, such as proportions of ingredients that make up a formulation or blend.[19]

Mode The most frequent value of a *variable.*[14]

Model The description relating a *response variable* to *predictor variable*(s) and including attendant assumptions.[19]

Model I analysis of variance (fixed model) An analysis of variance in which the *levels* of all *factors* are fixed rather than random selections over the range of versions to be studied for those factors.[30]

Model II analysis of variance (random model) An analysis of variance in which the *levels* of all *factors* are assumed to be selected at random over the range of versions to be studied for those factors.[30]

Moving average Let x_1, x_2, . . . denote individual observations. The moving average of span w at time i is

$$M_i = \frac{x_i + x_{i-1} + \ldots + x_{i-w+1}}{w}$$

M

At time period i, the oldest observation in the moving average set is dropped and the newest one added to the set.[26]

The variance, V, of the moving average M_i:

$$V(M_i) = \frac{1}{w^2} \sum_{j=1-w+1}^{i} V(x_j) = \frac{1}{w^2} \sum_{J=i-w+1}^{i} \sigma^2 = \frac{\sigma^2}{w}$$

Moving average chart (MA chart)
See Part II—Control Chart Guide

A *variables control chart* where the simple unweighted *moving average* of the last w observations is plotted and provides a convenient substitute for the $\bar{x}$ *chart*. A fixed number of samples, w, is required for averaging, but the choice of the interval for w may be difficult to optimize. The control *signal* is a single point out of limits. Additional tests are not appropriate because of the high correlation introduced between successive averages that share several common values. The MA chart is sensitive to trends and is sometimes used in conjunction with *individuals charts* and/or *MR charts*. It is, however, probably less effective than either the *CUSUM* or *exponentially weighted moving average* (EWMA) chart for this purpose.

Note 1: This chart is particularly useful when only one observation per *subgroup* is available. Examples are process characteristics such as temperature, pressure, and time.

Note 2: This chart has the disadvantage of an unweighted carryover effect lasting w points.

Each plotted point: $M_i = \dfrac{x_i + x_{i-1} + \ldots + x_{i-w+1}}{w}$

where M_i is the moving range of span w at time i. At time period i, the oldest observation in the moving average set is dropped and the newest one added to the set. For time periods where $i < w$, the average of the observations for periods 1, 2 ... i is plotted. Example (where $w = 4$):

Observation, i	x_i	M_i
1	9.45	9.45
2	7.99	8.72
3	9.29	8.91
4	11.66	9.5975
5	12.16	10.275

Central line: $\bar{x}$.

Control limits: $\bar{x} \pm \dfrac{3\sigma}{\sqrt{w}}$,

where $\bar{x}$ is the average of the individual variables

$$\bar{x} = \frac{x_1 + x_2 + \ldots + x_n}{n}$$

where $\bar{n}$ is the total number of samples, σ the standard deviation, and w is the moving range span.[11, 18, 26]

Moving range chart (*MR* chart)
See Part II—Control Chart Guide

A *control chart* that plots the absolute difference between the current and previous value. It often accompanies an *individuals chart* or *moving average chart*.

Note: The current observation replaces the oldest of the latest $n + 1$ observations.

Central line: $\bar{R}$

Control limits: $\text{UCL} = D_4\bar{R}$
$\text{LCL} = D_3\bar{R}$

where D_4 and D_3 are *control chart factors*. See Table 5.[11]

MR chart
See *moving range chart*.

MSA
See *measurement systems analysis*.

M

MTBF   See *mean time between failures.*

MTTF   See *mean time to failure.*

MTTR   See *mean time to repair.*

Multilevel continuous sampling   A continuous *acceptance sampling inspection* of consecutively produced items where two or more sampling inspection rates are either alternated with *100 percent inspection* or with each other depending on the quality of the observed *process* output.[18]

Multimodal   A *probability distribution* having more than one mode. See *bimodal* and *trimodal.*[30]

Multiple acceptance sampling inspection   An *acceptance sampling inspection* in which, after each *sample* has been inspected, a decision is made based upon defined decision rules to accept, not accept, or take another *sample.*

Note: For most multiple sampling plans, the largest number of samples that can be taken is specified with an accept or not accept decision being forced at that point.[18]

Multiple linear regression   See *regression analysis.*

Multivariate control chart   A variables *control chart* that allows plotting of more than one variable. These charts make use of the T^2 *statistic* to combine information from the *dispersion* and *mean* of several variables.[28]

M

n   See *sample size.*

N   See *lot size.*

Natural process limits   See *reference interval.*

Negative binomial distribution   A two-parameter, *discrete distribution.*[30]

Nested design   A design in which the second *factor* is nested within *levels* of the first factor and each succeeding factor is nested within levels of the previous factor.[19]

Nested factor   A *factor* (A) is nested within another factor (B) if the *levels* of A are different for every level of B. See *crossed factor.*[28]

Noise factor   In *robust parameter design,* a noise factor is a *predictor variable* that is hard to control or is not desired to control as part of the standard experimental conditions. In general, it is not desired to make inference on noise factors, but they are included in an experiment to broaden the conclusions regarding *control factors.*[30]

Z

Nominal scale   A scale with unordered, labeled categories, or a scale ordered by convention.

Examples: Type of defect, breed of dog, complaint category.

Note: It is possible to count by category, but not order or measure.[18]

Nonconforming unit   A *unit* with one or more *nonconformities.*[18]

Nonconformity   The nonfulfillment of a requirement. See notes under *defect.*[9]

Normal distribution (Gaussian distribution)   A *continuous,* symmetrical *frequency distribution* that produces a bell-shaped curve. The location *parameter* (x-axis) is the *mean, μ.* The scale parameter, σ, is the *standard deviation* of the normal distribution. When measurements have a normal distribution, 68.26% of the values lie within plus or minus one standard deviation of the mean ($\mu \pm 1\sigma$); 95.44% lie within plus or minus two standard deviations of the mean ($\mu \pm 2\sigma$); while 99.73% lie within plus or minus three standard deviations of the mean ($\mu \pm 3\sigma$).

The probability function is

$$f(x) = \frac{1}{\sigma\sqrt{2\pi}} \exp\left[-\frac{(x-\mu)^2}{2\sigma^2}\right]$$

where $-\infty < x < \infty$ and with parameters $-\infty < \mu < \infty$ and $\sigma > 0$. See Tables 1A–IH, 1J–1Q.[17]

Normal inspection   The inspection that is used when there is no reason to think that the quality level achieved by the *process* differs from a specified level. See *tightened inspection* and *loosened inspection.*[18]

Normal probability plot   See *probability plot.*

Z

np (number of affected or categorized units)   The total number of *units* in a *sample* in which an *event* of a given classification occurs. A unit (area of opportunity) is counted only once, even if several events of the same classification are encountered.

Note: In the quality field, the classification generally is number of *nonconforming units.*[4]

np chart (number of categorized units control chart)
See Part II—Control Chart Guide   An *attribute control chart* for number of *events* per unit where the opportunity is variable. (The *np* chart is for the number nonconforming whereas the *p chart* is for the proportion nonconforming.)

Note: Events of a particular type, for example, number of absentees or number of sales leads, form the count. In the quality field, events are often expressed as *nonconformities* and the variable opportunity relates to *subgroups* of variable size or variable amounts of material.

If a standard is given:

Central line: *np.*

Control limits: $np \pm 3\sqrt{np(1-p)}$

where *np* is the standard value of the events per unit and *p* is the standard value of the fraction nonconforming.

If no standard is given:

Central line: $\overline{np}$

Control limits: $\overline{np} \pm 3\sqrt{\overline{np}(1-\overline{p})}$

where $\overline{np}$ is the average value of the events per unit and $\overline{p}$ is the average value of the fraction nonconforming.[12, 18]

Z

Null hypothesis, H_0   The *hypothesis* in *tests of significance* that there is no difference (null) between the *population* of the *sample* and the specified population (or between the populations associated with each sample). The null hypothesis can never be proved true, but it can be shown (with specified risks or error) to be untrue; that is, a difference exists between the populations. If it is not disproved, one assumes there is no adequate reason to doubt it is true, and the null hypothesis is accepted. If the null hypothesis is shown to be untrue, then the *alternative hypothesis* is accepted.

Example: In a random sample of independent random variables with the same *normal distribution* with unknown *mean* and unknown *standard deviation,* a typical null hypothesis for the mean, μ, is that the mean is less than or equal to a given value, μ_0. The hypothesis is written as: $H_0 = \mu \le \mu_0$.[12, 17]

Observational unit The smallest entity on which a *response variable* is measured. It may be or not be the same as the *experimental unit.*[30]

Observed value The particular value of a *characteristic* determined as a result of a test or measurement.[4]

OC curve See *operating characteristic curve.*

Ogive A type of graph that represents the cumulative frequencies for the classes in a *frequency distribution.*[16]

One-tailed test A *hypothesis* test that involves only one of the tails of a distribution. Example: We wish to reject the *null hypothesis* H_0 only if the true *mean* is **larger** than μ_0.

$H_0: \mu = \mu_0$

$H_1: \mu < \mu_0$

A one-tailed test is either right-tailed or left-tailed, depending on the direction of the inequality of the *alternative hypothesis.*[16, 26]

Operating characteristic curve (OC curve) A curve showing the relationship between the *probability* of acceptance of product and the incoming quality level for a given *acceptance sampling plan.*

Note: Several terms in this glossary need to be referenced for better understanding of operating characteristic curves: α, β, *acceptance quality level, consumer's risk, indifference quality level, indifference zone, limiting quality level, probability of acceptance, probability of nonacceptance,* and *producer's risk.*[18]

Ordinal scale A scale with ordered, labeled categories.

Note 1: There is sometimes a blurred borderline between ordinal and *discrete scales.* When subjective opinion ratings such as excellent, very good, neutral, poor, and very poor are coded (as numbers 1–5), the apparent effect is conversion from an ordinal to a discrete scale. Such numbers should not be treated as ordinary numbers, however, because the distance between 1 and 2 may not be the same as between 2 and 3, or 3 and 4, and so forth. On the other hand, some categories that are ordered objectively according to magnitude, such as the Richter scale, which ranges from 0 to 8 according to the amount of energy release, could equally well be related to a discrete scale.

Note 2: Sometimes *nominal scales* are ordered by convention. An example is the blood groups A, B, and O, which are always stated in this order. The same is the case if different categories are denoted by single letters; they are then ordered by convention, according to the alphabet.[18]

Original inspection The *inspection* of a *lot,* or other amount, not previously inspected.

Note: This is in contrast, for example, to inspection of a *lot* that has previously been designated as not acceptable and is submitted again for inspection after having been further sorted, reprocessed, and so on.[18]

Orthogonal contrasts A set of *contrasts* whose coefficients satisfy the condition that, if multiplied in corresponding pairs, the sum of the products equals zero. See *contrast analysis.*[19]

Orthogonal design A design in which all pairs of *factors* at particular *levels* appear together an equal number of times. Examples include a wide variety of special designs such as a *Latin square, completely randomized factorial design,* and *fractional factorial design.* Statistical analysis of the results for *orthogonal designs* is relatively simple because each *main effect* and *interaction effect* may be evaluated independently.[12]

Out-of-control process A *process* operating with the presence of *special causes.* See *in-control process.*[29]

Outlier An extremely high or an extremely low data value compared to the rest of the data values. Great caution must be used when trying to identify an outlier.[30]

Output variable The variable representing the outcome of the *process.*[19]

P

p The ratio of the number of *units* in which at least one *event* of a given classification occurs, to the total number of units. A unit is counted only once even if several events of the same classification are encountered within it. p can also be expressed as a percent.[4]

$p_{.95}, p_{.50}, p_{.10}, p_{.05}$ The submitted quality in terms of the proportion of variant units for which the *probability of acceptance* is 0.95, 0.50, 0.10, 0.05 for a given *sampling plan*.[5]

p_1 The percent of *nonconforming* individual items occurring when the *process* is located at the *acceptable process level (APL)*.[4]

p_2 The percent of *nonconforming* individual items occurring when the *process* is located at the *rejectable process level (RPL)*.[4]

P See *probability*.

P_a See *probability of acceptance*.

P_r   See *probability of rejection.*

Parameter   A constant or coefficient describing some *characteristic* of a *population.* Examples: *standard deviation* and *mean.*[14]

Pareto chart   A graphical tool based on the *Pareto principle* for ranking causes from most significant to least significant.[1]

Pareto principle   The principle, named after 19th century economist Vilfredo Pareto, suggests that most *effects* come from relatively few causes; that is, about 80 percent of effects come from about 20 percent of the possible *causes.*[1]

Partially nested design   A *nested design* in which several *factors* may be *crossed* as in *factorial experiments* and other factors nested within the crossed combinations.[19]

Parts per million (PPM or ppm)   A measurement that is expressed by dividing the data set into 1,000,000 or 10^6 equal groups.[30]

Part-to-part variation   The variability of the data due to measurement items rather than the *measurement system.* This *variation* is typically estimated from the measurement items used in a study, but could be estimated from a *representative sample* of product.[30]

p chart   See *proportion chart.*

P

Pearson's correlation coefficient	See *correlation coefficient.*
Percentile	The division of the data set into 100 equal groups.[30]
Plackett-Burman design	An *experimental design* used where there are many *factors* to study. It only studies the *main effects* and is primarily used as a *screening design* before applying other types of designs. In general, Plackett-Burman designs are two-level, but three-, five-, and seven-level designs are available. They allow for efficient estimation of the main effects, but assume that interactions can initially be ignored.[30]
Poisson distribution	The Poisson distribution describes occurrences of isolated events in a continuum of time or space. It is a one-parameter, *discrete distribution* depending only on the *mean.*[30]
Pooled standard deviation	A *standard deviation* value resulting from some combination of individual standard deviation values. It is most often used when individual standard deviation values are similar in magnitude and can be denoted by s_p. See *t-test (two sample).*[30]
Population	The entire set (totality) of *units,* quantity of material, or observations under consideration. A population may be real and finite, real and infinite, or completely hypothetical. See *sample.*[17, 18]
Population covariance	See *covariance.*

Population mean (*μ*)   The true *mean* of the *population,* represented by μ *(mu).* The *sample mean,* $\bar{x}$, is a common estimator of the population mean.[30]

Population standard deviation   See *standard deviation.*

Population variance   See *variance.*

Power   The equivalent to one minus the *probability* of a *type II error* $(1 - \beta)$. A higher power is associated with a higher probability of finding a statistically significant difference. Lack of power usually occurs with smaller sample sizes.[17]

Power curve   The curve showing the relationship between the *probability* $(1 - \beta)$ of rejecting the *hypothesis* that a sample belongs to a given *population* with a given *characteristic*(s) and the actual population value of that characteristic(s).

Note: If β, the probability of accepting the hypothesis, is used instead of $(1 - \beta)$, the curve is called an *operating characteristic (OC) curve.*[4]

***Pp* (process performance index)**   An index describing *process performance* in relation to specified *tolerance*

$$Pp = \frac{U - L}{6s}$$

s is used for *standard deviation* instead of σ since both *random* and *special causes* may be present.

Note: A *state of statistical control* is not required.[18]

Ppk (minimum process performance index)

The smaller of *upper process performance index* and *lower process performance index.*[18]

Ppk$_L$ (lower process performance index or PPL)

An index describing *process performance* in relation to the *lower specification limit.* For a symmetrical normal distribution:

$$Ppk_L = \frac{\bar{x} - L}{3s}$$

where *s* is defined under *Pp.*[18]

Ppk$_U$ (upper process performance index or PPU)

An index describing *process performance* in relation to the *upper specification limit.* For a symmetrical *normal distribution:*

$$Ppk_U = \frac{U - \bar{x}}{3s}$$

where *s* is defined under *Pp.*[18]

PPL   See *Ppk$_L$.*

PPM (or ppm)   See *parts per million.*

PPU   See *Ppk$_U$.*

Precision   The closeness of agreement between randomly selected individual measurements or test results. See *repeatability* and *reproducibility.*[12]

Precision to tolerance ratio (PTR)

A measure of the *capability* of the *measurement system.* It can be calculated by

$$PTR = \frac{5.15 \times \hat{\sigma}_{ms}}{USL - LSL}$$

where $\hat{\sigma}_{ms}$ is the estimated *standard deviation* of the total measurement system variability.

In general, reducing the PTR will yield an improved measurement system.[30]

Predicted value The prediction of future observations based on the formulated *model.*[30]

Prediction interval Similar to a *confidence interval,* it is an interval based on the *predicted value* that is likely to contain the values of future observations. It will be wider than the confidence interval because it contains bounds on individual observations rather than a bound on the *mean* of a group of observations.[30]

Predictor variable A *variable* that can contribute to the explanation of the outcome of an experiment.[19]

Probability (*P*) The chance of an *event* occurring.[30]

Probability distribution A function that completely describes the probabilities with which specific values occur. The values may be from a *discrete scale* or a *continuous scale.*[30]

Probability of acceptance (*P*_a) The *probability* that when using a given *acceptance sampling plan,* a *lot* will be accepted when the *lot* or *process* is of a specific quality level.[18]

Probability of nonacceptance See *probability of rejection.*

P

Probability of rejection (P_r)	The probability that when using a given *acceptance sampling plan,* a *lot* will not be accepted when *the lot* or *process* is of a specified quality level.[18]

Probability plot	The plot of ranked data versus the *sample* cumulative frequency on a special vertical scale. The special scale is chosen (that is, normal, lognormal, and so on) so that the *cumulative distribution* is a straight line.[30]

Process	A series of interrelated steps consisting of resources and activities that transform inputs into outputs and work together to a common end. A process can be graphically represented using a *flowchart.*[30]

Process average	See *sample mean* or *population mean.*

Process capability	The calculated inherent variability of a *characteristic* of a product. It represents the best performance of the *process* over a period of stable operations. Process capability is expressed as $6\hat{\sigma}$, where $\hat{\sigma}$ is the *sample standard deviation* (short-term component of variation) of the process under a *state of statistical control.*[11]

Process capability index	A single-number assessment of ability to meet *specification limits* on the quality *characteristic*(s) of interest. The indices compare the variability of the characteristic to the specification limits. Three basic process capability indices are *Cp, Cpk,* and *Cpm.* Note: Since there are many different types and variations of process capability indices, details are given under the symbol for the specific type of index.[23]

Process control   *Process* management that is focused on fulfilling process requirements. Process control is the methodology for keeping a process within boundaries and minimizing the variation of a process.[12, 18]

Process performance   The statistical measure of the outcome of a *characteristic* from a *process* that may *not* have been demonstrated to be in a *state of statistical control.*

Note: Use this measure cautiously since it may contain a component of variability from *special causes* of unpredictable value. It differs from *process capability* because a state of statistical control is not required.[18]

Process performance index   A single-number assessment of ability to meet *specification limits* on the quality *characteristic*(s) of interest. The indices compare the variability of the characteristic to the specification limits. Three basic process capability indices are *Pp, Ppk,* and *Ppm.*

Note: Since there are many different types and variations of process capability indices, details are given under the symbol for the specific type of index.[23]

Process quality   A statistical measure of the quality of product from a given *process.* The measure may be an *attribute (qualitative)* or a *variable (quantitative).* A common measure of process quality is the fraction or proportion of nonconforming units in the process.[30]

Process to tolerance ratio   See *precision to tolerance ratio.*

Process variable   See *variable.*

Producer's risk (α)   The *probability* of nonacceptance when the quality level has a value stated by the *acceptance sampling plan* as acceptable.

Note 1: Such nonacceptance is a *type I error.*

Note 2: Producer's risk is usually designated as *α.*

Note 3: Quality level could relate to fraction nonconforming and acceptable to *AQL.*

Note 4: Interpretation of the producer's risk requires knowledge of the stated quality level.[18]

Proportion chart (p chart or percent categorized units control chart)

See Part II—Control Chart Guide

An *attribute control chart* for number of *units* of a given classification per total number of units in the *sample* expressed as either a proportion or percent.

Note 1: The classification often takes the form of *nonconforming units.*

Note 2: The *p* chart applies particularly when the sample size is variable.

Note 3: If the *upper control limit (UCL)* calculates ≥ 1 there is no UCL; or if the *lower control limit (LCL)* calculates ≤ 0, there is no LCL.

a. When the fraction nonconforming is known, or is a specified standard value:

Central line: *p.*

Control limits: $p \pm 3\sqrt{\dfrac{p(1-p)}{n}}$

where *p* is known fraction nonconforming (or standard value).

Plotted value: $\hat{p}$

where $\hat{p}$ is the *sample* fraction nonconforming:

$\hat{p} = D/n$ where D is the number of product units that are nonconforming and n is the sample size.

b. When the fraction nonconforming is not known:

Central line: $\bar{p}$.

Control limits: $\bar{p} \pm 3\sqrt{\dfrac{\bar{p}(1-\bar{p})}{n}}$

where $\bar{p}$ is the *average* value of the fraction of the classification (often average percent nonconforming), and n is the total number of units.

These limits are considered trial limits.

c. For variable sample size:

Central line: $\bar{p}$.

Control limits: $\bar{p} \pm 3\sqrt{\dfrac{\bar{p}(1-\bar{p})}{n_i}}$

where n_i is varying sample size.

Plotted value: $\hat{p}$

where $\hat{p}$ is the *sample* fraction nonconforming:

$\hat{p} = D_i/n$ where D_i is the number of nonconforming units in sample i, and n is the sample size.[12, 18, 26]

Proportions, tests for   Tests for proportions include the *binomial distribution*. See *binomial confidence interval*, and *z-test for two proportions*.

The *standard deviation* for proportions is given by

$$s = \sqrt{\dfrac{p(1-p)}{n}}$$

where p is the *population* proportion and n is the *sample* size.[30]

PTR   See *precision to tolerance ratio.*

p-value   The *probability* of observing the *test statistic* value or any other value at least as unfavorable to the *null hypothesis.*[17]

Q_1 See *first quartile.*

Q_2 See *second quartile.*

Q_3 See *third quartile.*

QA   See *quality assurance.*

QC   See *quality control.*

Qualitative data   See *attribute data.*

Quality   The degree to which a set of inherent *characteristics* fulfills requirements.[9]

Quality assurance (QA)   The part of *quality management* focused on providing confidence that quality requirements will be fulfilled.[9]

Quality control (QC)   The part of *quality management* focused on fulfilling quality requirements.[9]

Quality management   Coordinated activities to direct and control an organization with regard to *quality.* Such activities generally include establishment of the quality policy, quality objectives, quality planning, *quality control, quality assurance,* and quality improvement.[9]

Quantitative data   See *variable data.*

Quartiles   Division of a distribution into four groups, denoted by Q_1 (first quartile), Q_2 (second quartile), and Q_3 (third quartile). Note that Q_1 is the same as the 25th *percentile,* Q_2 is the same as the 50th percentile and the *median,* and Q_3 corresponds to the 75th percentile.[30]

R

r See *correlation coefficient.*

R See *range.*

$\bar{R}$ (pronounced r-bar) The *average* range calculated from the set of *subgroup* ranges under consideration. See *range.*[30]

R^2 See *coefficient of determination.*

R_{adj}^2 R^2 *(coefficient of determination)* adjusted for *degrees of freedom.*

$$R_{adj}^2 = 1 - \frac{\text{Sum of squares error} / (n - p)}{\text{Sum of squares total} / (n - 1)}$$

where p is the number of coefficients fit in the *regression* equation.[25]

Random cause The source of *process* variation that is inherent in a process over time. Also called *common cause* or *chance cause.*

Note: In a process subject only to random cause variation, the variation is predictable within statistically established limits.[18]

Random factor   A *factor* that uses *levels* that are selected at random from a large or infinite number of possibilities. In general, inference is made to other levels of the same factor. See also *fixed factor.*[28]

Random model   A *model* that contains only random *factors.*[30]

Random sampling   A sampling where a *sample* of *n* sampling *units* is taken from a *population* in such a way that each of the possible combinations of *n* sampling units has a particular probability of being taken.[18]

Random variation   Variation from *random causes.*[18]

Randomization   The process used to assign *treatments* to *experimental units* so that each experimental unit has an equal chance of being assigned a particular *treatment.* Randomization validates the assumptions made in statistical analysis and prevents unknown biases from impacting the conclusions.[19]

Randomized block design   An *experimental design* consisting of *b blocks* with *t treatments* assigned via *randomization* to the *experimental units* within each block. This is a method for controlling the variability of experimental units. For the *completely randomized design,* no stratification of the experimental units is made. In the randomized block design, the treatments are randomly allotted within each block; that is, the randomization is restricted.[19]

Randomized block factorial design   A *factorial design* run in a *randomized block design* where each *block* includes a complete set of factorial combinations.[19]

Range (*R*)   A measure of *dispersion,* which is the absolute difference between the highest and lowest *value* in a given *subgroup:*

R = highest observed value – lowest observed value.[11, 12]

Range chart (*R* chart)
See Part II—Control Chart Guide   A *variables control chart* that plots the range of a *subgroup* to detect shifts in the subgroup range. See *range (R).*

Central line: $\overline{R}$.

Upper control limit: $D_4\overline{R}$.

Lower control limit: $D_3\overline{R}$.

where $\overline{R}$ is the average range; D_3 and D_4 are factors from Table 5.

Note: A range chart is used when the sample size is small; if the sample is larger (generally >10 to 12), the *s* chart should be used.[7, 8]

Rational subgroup   A *subgroup* wherein the variation is presumed to be only from *random causes.*[18]

***R* chart**   See *range chart.*

Re   See *rejection number.*

Rectifying inspection   An inspection of all, or a specified number of, items in a *lot* or other amount previously rejected on *acceptance sampling* inspection, as a consequence of which all *nonconforming items* are removed or replaced.[18]

Reduced inspection   An *inspection* less severe than *normal inspection,* to which the latter is switched when inspection results of a predetermined number of *lots* indicate that the quality level achieved by the *process* is better than that specified.[18]

Redundancy   The existence of more than one means for accomplishing a given function. Each means of accomplishing the function need not necessarily be identical.[24]

Reference interval   The interval bounded by the 99.865% distribution fractile, $X_{99.865\%}$, and the 0.135% distribution fractile, $X_{0.135\%}$, expressed by the difference $X_{99.865\%} - X_{0.135\%}$.

Note 1: This term is used only as an arbitrary, but standardized, basis for defining the *process performance index, Pp,* and *process capability index, Cp.*

Note 2: For a *normal distribution,* the reference interval may be expressed in terms of *standard* deviations as 6σ or $6s$ when estimated from a sample.

Note 3: For a nonnormal distribution, the reference interval may be estimated by appropriate probability scales or from the sample kurtosis and sample skewness.

Note 4: The conditions prevailing must always be stated: *process capability* conditions (a *state of statistical control* required) or *process performance* conditions (a state of statistical control not required).[18]

Regression   See *regression analysis.*

Regression analysis   A technique that uses *predictor variable(s)* to predict the *variation* in a *response variable.* Regression analysis uses the method of *least* *squares* to determine the values of the *linear regression coefficients* and the corresponding *model*. It is particularly pertinent when the predictor variables are *continuous* and emphasis is on creating a predictive model. When some of the predictor variables are *discrete, analysis of variance* or *analysis of covariance* is likely a more appropriate method.

This resulting model can then test the resulting predictions for statistical significance against an appropriate *null hypothesis* model. The model also gives some sense of the degree of *linearity* present in the data.

When only one predictor variable is used, regression analysis is often referred to as *simple linear regression.* A simple linear regression model commonly uses a *linear regression equation* expressed as $Y = \beta_0 + \beta_1 x + \varepsilon$, where Y is the response, x is the value of the predictor variable, β_0 and β_1 are the linear regression coefficients, and ε is the random error term. β_0 is often called the *intercept* and β_1 is often called the *slope.*

When multiple predictor variables are used, regression is referred to as *multiple linear regression.* For example, a multiple linear regression model with three predictor variables commonly uses a linear regression equation expressed as $Y = \beta_0 + \beta_1 x_1 + \beta_2 x_2 + \beta_3 x_3 + \varepsilon$, where Y is the response, x_1, x_2, x_3 are the values of the predictor variables, β_0, β_1, β_2, and β_3 are the linear regression coefficients, and ε is the random error term.

The random error terms in regression analysis are often assumed to be normally distributed with a constant *variance.* These assumptions can be readily checked through *residual analysis* or *residual plots.*[12, 19, 30]

See *regression coefficients, tests for.*

Regression coefficients, tests for   A test of the individual *linear regression coefficients* to determine their significance in the *model*. These tests assume that the *response variable* is normally distributed for a fixed level of the *predictor variable,* the variability of the response variable is the same regardless of the value of the predictor variable, and that the predictor variable can be measured without error. See *regression analysis.*[30]

Reject (acceptance sampling usage)   To decide that a *batch, lot,* or quantity of product, material, or service has not been shown to satisfy the requirement criteria based on the information obtained from the *sample*(s).

Note: In *acceptance sampling,* the words "to reject" generally are used to mean to not accept, without direct implication of product usability. Lots that are rejected may be scrapped; sorted (with or without *nonconforming units* being replaced); reworked; reevaluated against more specific usability criteria; held for additional information; and so on. Because the common language usage "reject" often results in an inference of unsafe or unusable product, it is recommended that the words "not accept" be used instead.[4]

Rejectable process level (RPL)   The *process* level that forms the inner boundary of the rejectable process zone.

Note: In the case of two-sided *tolerances,* upper and lower rejectable process levels will be designated *URPL* and *LRPL.* (These need not be symmetrical around the standard level.)[4, 18]

Rejectable process zone   See *rejectable process level.*

Rejectable quality level (RQL)

See *limiting quality level (LQL)*.[4]

Rejection number (Re)

The smallest number of *nonconformities* or *nonconforming units* found in the *sample* by *acceptance sampling by attributes* that requires the *lot* to be not accepted, as given in the *acceptance sampling plan*.[18]

Relative frequency

The number of occurrences or *observed values* in a specified class divided by the total number of occurrences or observed values.[17]

Reliability

The probability that an item can perform its intended function for a specified interval under stated conditions.[24]

Repairability

The probability that a failed system will be restored to operable condition in a specified active repair time.[33]

Repeatability

Precision under conditions where independent measurement results are obtained with the same method on identical measurement items by the same operator using the same equipment within a short period of time.[18]

Repeated measures

The measurement of a *response variable* more than once under similar conditions. Repeated measures allow one to determine the inherent variability in the *measurement system*. Also known as *duplication* or repetition.[30]

Replicate

A single repetition of the experiment. See also *replication*.[19]

Replication   Performance of an experiment more than once for a given set of *predictor variables.* Each of the repetitions of the experiment is called a *replicate.* Replication differs from *repeated measures* in that it is a repeat of the entire experiment for a given set of *predictor variables,* not just a repeat of measurements on the same experiment.

Note: Replication increases the precision of the estimates of the *effects* in an experiment. It is more effective when all elements contributing to the *experimental error* are included. In some cases replication may be limited to *repeated measures* under essentially the same conditions. In other cases, replication may be deliberately different, though similar, in order to make the results more general.[12, 19]

Representative sample   A *sample* that by itself or as part of a sampling system or protocol exhibits *characteristics* and properties of the *population* sampled.[10]

Reproducibility   *Precision* under conditions where independent measurement results are obtained with the same method on identical measurement items with different operators using different equipment.[18]

Resample   An analysis of an additional *sample* from a *lot.* Resampling not included in the design of the *control chart* delays *corrective action* and changes the risk levels on which control charts are calculated. Resampling should not be used to replace sample results that indicate a *nonconformity,* but it is appropriate if the sample was known to be defective or invalid or to obtain additional information on the material sampled.[11, 13]

Residual analysis The method of using *residuals* to determine appropriateness of assumptions made by a statistical method.[30]

Residual plot A plot used in *residual analysis* to determine appropriateness of assumptions made by a statistical method. Common forms include a plot of the *residuals* versus the *observed values* or a plot of the residuals versus the *predicted values* from the fitted model.[30]

Residuals The difference between the observed result and the *predicted value* (estimated treatment response) based on empirically determined model.[19]

Resistant line A line derived from using *medians* in fitting lines to data.[25]

Resolution 1: The smallest measurement increment that can be detected by the *measurement system.* 2: In the context of *experimental design,* resolution refers to the level of *confounding* in a *fractional factorial design.* For example in a resolution III design, the *main effects* are confounded with the two-way *interaction effects.*[19, 30]

Response surface design A design intended to investigate the functional relationship between a *response variable* and a set of *predictor variables.* It is generally most useful when the predictor variables are continuous. See *Box-Behnken design* and *central composite design.*[19]

Response surface methodology (RSM) A methodology that uses *design of experiments, regression analysis,* and optimization techniques to determine the best relationship between a *response variable* and a set of *predictor variables.*[30]

Response variable   A variable representing the outcome of an experiment.[19]

Resubmitted lot   A *lot* that previously has been designated as not acceptable and that is submitted again for acceptance inspection after having been further tested, sorted, reprocessed, and so on.

Note: Any *nonconforming units* discovered during the interim action must be removed, replaced, or reworked.[4]

Risk, consumer's (β)   See *consumer's risk (β).*

Risk, producer's (α)   See *producer's risk (α).*

Robust   A *characteristic* of a *statistic* or statistical method. A robust statistical method still gives reasonable results even though the standard assumptions are not met. A robust statistic is unchanged by the presence of unusual data points or *outliers.*[30]

Robust parameter design   A design that aims to reduce the performance variation of a product or *process* by choosing the setting of its *control factors* to make it less sensitive to variability from *noise factors.*[30]

Root cause analysis   The *process* of identifying *causes.* Many systems are available for analyzing data to ultimately determine the root cause.[30]

RPL   See *rejectable process level.*

RQL   See *rejectable quality level.*

RSM   See *response surface methodology.*

Run   See *experimental run.*

Run (control chart usage)   An uninterrupted sequence of occurrences of the same *attribute* or *event* in a series of observations, or a consecutive set of successively increasing (run up) or successively decreasing (run down) values in a series of *variable* measurements.

Note: In some *control chart* applications, a run might be considered a series of a specified number of points consecutively plotting above or below the *center line,* or five consecutive points, three of which fall outside warning limits.[4]

Running weighted average   An equation used to smooth data sequences by replacing each data value with the *average* of the data values around it and with weights multiplied in each averaging operation. The weights sum to 1.[30]

S

σ **(sigma)**   See *standard deviation.*

σ^2 **(sigma square)**   See *variance.*

$\sigma_{\bar{x}}$ **(sigma x-bar)**   The *standard deviation* (or *standard error*) of $\bar{x}$.[30]

σ_{wt} The *standard deviation* of the *exponentially weighted moving average:*

$$\sigma_{w_t} = \sigma\sqrt{\lambda/(2-\lambda)} \quad \text{[Asymptotic value]}$$

$$\sigma_{w_t} = \sigma\sqrt{\lambda/(2-\lambda)\left[1-(1-\lambda)^{2i}\right]} \quad \text{[Initial values]}.$$

See *exponentially weighted moving average chart.*[30]

$\hat{\sigma}$ **(sigma-hat)**   In general, any estimate of the *population standard deviation.* There are various ways to get this estimate depending on the particular application.[30]

s See *standard deviation.*

96

s^2 See *variance.*

s_p See *pooled standard deviation, t-test (two sample),* and *proportion, tests for.*

Sample   A group of *units,* portions or material, or observations taken from a larger collection of units, quantity of material, or observations that serves to provide information that may be used for making a decision concerning the larger quantity (the *population*).

Note 1: The sample may be the actual units or material or the observations collected from them. The decision may or may not involve taking action on the units or material, or on the *process.*

Note 2: *Sampling plans* are schemes set up statistically in order to provide a sampling system with minimum bias.

Note 3: There are many different ways, random and nonrandom, to select a sample. In survey sampling, sampling units are often selected with a probability proportional to the size of a known variable, giving a biased sample.[14, 18]

Sample covariance   See *covariance.*

Sample mean   The sample mean (or *average*) is the sum of random variables in a *random sample* divided by the number in the sum. It is generally designated by the symbol $\bar{x}$.

Note: The sample mean considered as a *statistic* is an estimator for the *population mean.* A common synonym is the *arithmetic mean.*[17]

Sample size *(n)*   The number of sampling *units* in a *sample*.

Note: In a multistage sample, the sample size is the total number of sampling *units* at the conclusion of the final stage of sampling.[18]

Sample standard deviation   See *standard deviation*.

Sample variance   See *variance*.

Sampling interval   In systematic sampling, the sampling interval is the fixed interval of time, output, running hours, and so on, between samples.[4]

Sampling plan (acceptance sampling usage)   A specific plan that states the *sample size*(s) to be used and the associated criteria for accepting the *lot*.

Note: The sampling plan does not contain the rules on how to take the sample.[3]

Sampling scheme (acceptance sampling usage)   A combination of *sampling plans* with rules for changing from one plan to another.[3]

Saturated design   A design where the number of *factors* studied is nearly equal to the number of *experimental runs*. Saturated designs do not allow for a check of model adequacy or estimation of higher-order *effects*. This design should only be used if the cost of doing more experimental runs is prohibitive.[19]

Scatter plot or diagram   A plot of two variables, one on the y-axis and the other on the x-axis. The resulting graph allows visual examination for patterns to deter-mine if the variables show any relationship or if there is just random scatter. This pattern or lack thereof aids in choosing the appropriate type of model for estimation.[30]

s chart   See *standard deviation chart.*

Screening design   An experiment intended to identify a subset of the collection of *factors* for subsequent study. Examples include *fractional factorial designs* or *Plackett-Burman designs.*[19]

Second quartile (Q₂)   The 50th *percentile* or the *median.* See *quartiles.*[30]

Sequential sampling   An *acceptance sampling inspection* in which, after each item has been inspected, the decision to accept the *lot,* not accept the lot, or to inspect another item is taken based on the cumulative sampling evidence.

Note 1: The decision is made according to defined rules.

Note 2: The total number of items to be inspected is not fixed in advance but a maximum number is often agreed upon.[18]

Serviceability   The ease or difficulty with which equipment can be repaired.[33]

Shewhart control chart   A *control chart* with *Shewhart control limits* intended primarily to distinguish between variation due to *random causes* and variation due to *special causes.*[18]

Shewhart control limits   *Control limits* based on empirical evidence and economic considerations, placed about the *center line* at a distance of ± 3 *standard deviations* of the *statistic* under consideration and used to evaluate whether or not it is a *stable process.*[18]

Signal   An indication on a *control chart* that a *process* is not *stable* or that a shift has occurred. Typical indicators are points outside *control limits, runs, trends,* cycles, patterns, and so on. See also *average run length.*[30]

Significance level   The maximum *probability* of rejecting the *null hypothesis* when in fact it is true.

Note: The significance level is usually designated by α and should be set before beginning the test.[17]

Significance tests   Significance tests are a method of deciding, with certain predetermined risks of error, (1) whether the *population* associated with a *sample* differs from the one specified; (2) whether the population associated with each of two samples differ; or (3) whether the populations associated with each of more than two samples differ. Significance testing is equivalent to the testing of *hypotheses.* Therefore, a clear statement of the *null hypothesis, alternative hypotheses,* and predetermined selection of a *confidence level* are required.

Note: The level of significance is the maximum *probability* of committing a *type I error.* This probability is symbolized by α, that is, P (type I error) $= \alpha$.

See *confidence interval; means, tests for;* and *proportions, tests for.*[14, 16]

Simple linear regression   See *regression analysis.*

Single sampling   An *acceptance sampling inspection* in which
(acceptance   the decision to accept, according to a defined
sampling usage)   rule, is based on the inspection results obtained
from a single *sample* of predetermined size, *n.*[18]

Single-level   A continuous *acceptance sampling inspection*
continuous sampling   of consecutively produced items where a
single fixed sampling rate is alternated with
100 percent inspection depending on the
quality of the observed *process* output.[18]

Six Sigma   A methodology that provides businesses with
the tools to improve the capability of their
business processes.[1]

Skewness   A measure of symmetry about the *mean.*
For a *normal distribution,* skewness is zero
because the distribution is symmetric.[30]

Skip-lot sampling   An *acceptance sampling inspection* in which
some *lots* in a series are accepted without
inspection, when the sampling results for a
stated number of immediately preceding lots
meet stated criteria.[18]

Slope   See *regression analysis.*

SPC   See *statistical process control.*

Special cause   A source of process variation other than
inherent process variation.

Note 1: Sometimes special cause is considered synonymous with *assignable cause,* but a special cause is assignable only when it is specifically identified.

Note 2: A special cause arises because of specific circumstances that are not always present. Therefore, in a process subject to special causes, the magnitude of the variation over time is unpredictable.[18]

Specification limit(s) The limiting value(s) stated for a *characteristic*. See *tolerance.*[18]

Split-plot design A design where there is a hierarchical structure in the *experimental units*. One or more principal *factors* are studied using the largest experimental unit, often called a whole plot. The whole plots are subdivided into smaller experimental units, often called split-plots. Additional factors are studied using each of the split-plots. This type of design is frequently used with a principal factor whose levels are not easily changed, and the other factors can be varied readily within the runs assigned to the principal factor.[19]

Spread A term sometimes synonymous with *variation* or *dispersion.*[30]

Stable process A *process* that is predictable within limits; a process that is subject only to *random causes*. (This is also known as a *state of statistical control.*)

Note 1: A stable process will generally behave as though the results are simple random samples from the same *population*.

Note 2: This state does not imply that the *random variation* is large or small, within or outside of *specification limits,* but rather that the variation is predictable using statistical techniques.

Note 3: The *process capability* of a stable process is usually improved by fundamental changes that reduce or remove some of the *random causes* present and/or adjusting the *mean* toward the *target* value.[18, 27]

Staggered nested design A *nested design* in which the *nested factors* are run within only a subset of the *levels* of the first or succeeding *factors.*[19]

Standard deviation A measure of the *spread* of the *process* output or the spread of a sampling *statistic* from the process. When working with the *population,* the standard deviation is usually denoted by σ (sigma). When working with a *sample* the standard deviation is usually denoted by s. They are calculated as

$$\sigma = \sqrt{\frac{1}{n}\sum(x-\mu)^2}$$

$$s = \sqrt{\frac{1}{n-1}\sum(x-\bar{x})^2}$$

where n is the number of data points in the sample or population, μ is the *population mean,* x is the observed value of the quality characteristic, and $\bar{x}$ is the sample mean. See *standard error.*

Note: Standard deviation can also be calculated by taking the square root of the *population variance* or *sample variance.*[17]

Standard deviation chart (*s* chart)
See Part II—Control Chart Guide A *variables control chart* of the *standard deviation* of the results within a *subgroup.* It replaces *range chart* for large subgroup samples (rule of thumb is subgroup size 10 to 12).

Central line: $\bar{s}$

Upper control limit: $B_4\bar{s}$

Lower control limit: $B_3\bar{s}$

where $\bar{s}$ is the average value of the standard deviation of the subgroups and B_3 and B_4 are factors from Table 5. See *standard deviation*.[8, 12]

Standard deviation of proportions

See *proportions, tests for.*

Standard deviation of the intercept

See *tests for regression coefficients.*

Standard deviation of the slope

See *tests for regression coefficients.*

Standard deviation of *u* or *c/n*

See *u chart.*

Standard error

The *standard deviation* of a *sample statistic* or estimator. When dealing with sample statistics, we either refer to the standard deviation of the sample statistic or to its standard error.[17]

Standard error of predicted values

A measure of the variation of individual predicted values of the *dependent variable* about the *population* value for a given value of the *predictor variable*. This includes the variability of individuals about the sample regression line and the sample line about the population line. It measures the variability of individual observations and can be used to calculate a *prediction interval*.[14]

Star point   *Experimental runs* in *response surface designs* that are neither *center points* nor *cube points.* They are usually farther away from the center of the design space. Star points are most often used to fit higher-order models to experimental data.[19]

State of statistical control   See *stable process.*

Statistic   A quantity calculated from a sample of observations, most often to form an estimate of some *population parameter.*[14]

Statistical measure   A *statistic* or mathematical function of a statistic.[14]

Statistical process control (SPC)   The use of statistical techniques such as *control charts* to reduce variation, increase knowledge about the *process,* and to steer the process in the desired way.

Note 1: SPC operates most efficiently by controlling variation of the process or in-process *characteristics* that correlate with a final product characteristic and/or by increasing the *robustness* of the process against this variation.

Note 2: A supplier's final product characteristic can be a process characteristic of the next downstream supplier's process.[18]

Statistical thinking   A philosophy of learning and action based on the following fundamental principles:

- All work occurs in a system of interconnected processes.

- *Variation* exists in all *processes.*

- Understanding and reducing variation are keys to success.[12]

Statistical tolerance interval
An interval estimator determined from a random sample so as to provide a specified level of confidence that the interval covers at least a specified proportion of the sampled *population.*[17]

Stem
See *stem-and-leaf diagram.*

Stem-and-leaf diagram
A diagram used to display the shape and *spread* of *sample* data. The plot looks somewhat like a *histogram* on its side, although, instead of bars, it has digits from the actual data values that indicate the frequency of each bin (row). The display has three columns.

1. The leaf (right). Each value in the leaf column represents a digit from one observation. The "leaf unit" (declared above the plot) specifies which digit is used. In the example, the leaf unit is 1. The first value is 76. Thus, the leaf value is 6.

2. The stem (middle). The stem value represents the digit immediately to the left of the leaf digit. In the example, the stem value is 7. In the next row the stem value is 8. That indicates that the leaves in that row are greater than or equal to 80, but less than 85.

3. The count (left). If the *median* value for the sample is included in a row, the count for

that row is enclosed in parentheses. In the example, the median is 99.5 and therefore no count is enclosed in parentheses. The values for rows above and below the median are cumulative. The count for a row above the median represents the total count for that row and the rows above it. The value for a row below the median represents the total count for that row and the rows below it.[20, 25, 31, 32]

A sample stem-and-leaf diagram. N = 100
Leaf unit = 1

1	7	6
6	8	11133
11	8	55889
33	9	0011111122223333334444
50	9	55677777778889999
50	10	0011122222222233333444
28	10	556667778999
16	11	01112222234
5	11	558
2	12	03

Stratified sampling   A *sampling* such that portions of the *sample* are drawn from different strata and each stratum is sampled with at least one sampling *unit.*

Note 1: In some cases, the portions are specified proportions determined in advance, however, in post-stratified sampling the specified proportions would not be known in advance.

Note 2: Items from each stratum are often selected by random sampling.[18]

Subgroup (control chart usage) A group of data plotted as a single point on a control chart. See *rational subgroup*.[30]

Switching rules Instruction within an *acceptance sampling scheme* for changing from one *acceptance sampling plan* to another of greater or lesser severity of sampling based on demonstrated quality level.

Normal, tightened, reduced inspection, or discontinuation of inspection are examples of severity of sampling.[3, 18]

T^2 (Hotelling's T^2) A multivariate test that is a generalization of the *t-test*.[30]

Taguchi design See *robust parameter design*.

Target value The preferred reference value of a *characteristic* stated in a specification.[18]

t-confidence interval for means (one-sample) When there is an unknown *mean μ* and unknown *variance σ^2*. For a *two-tailed test*, a $100(1 - \alpha)\%$ two-sided confidence interval on the true mean:

$$\bar{x} - t_{a/2,n-1}\frac{s}{\sqrt{n}} \leq \mu \leq \bar{x} + t_{a/2,n-1}\frac{s}{\sqrt{n}}$$

where $t_{a/2,n-1}$ denotes the percentage point of the *t distribution* with $n - 1$ *degrees of freedom* such that $P\{t_{n-1} \leq t_{a/2,n-1}\} = \alpha/2$.

See *confidence interval*.[26]

t-confidence interval for means (two-sample) When there is a difference in *means (μ_1 and μ_2)*, and the *variances* are unknown. The combined or pooled estimate of the common variance, s_p is:

$$s_p^2 = \frac{(n_1 - 1)s_1^2 + (n_2 - 1)s_2^2}{n_1 + n_2 - 2}$$

The $100(1 - \alpha)\%$ two-sided confidence interval on μ_1 and μ_2 is

$$\left(\bar{x}_1 - \bar{x}_2\right) - t_{\alpha/2, n_1 + n_2 - 2} S_p \sqrt{\frac{1}{n_1} + \frac{1}{n_2}} \leq \mu_1 + \mu_2 \leq$$

$$\left(\bar{x}_1 - \bar{x}_2\right) + t_{\alpha/2, n_1 + n_2 - 2} S_p \sqrt{\frac{1}{n_1} + \frac{1}{n_2}}$$

where $\bar{x}_1$ and $\bar{x}_2$ are the sample means $t_{\alpha/2}$ is the value from a *t-distribution* table where α is $1 - confidence\ level/100$.

See *confidence interval.*[26]

t distribution   A theoretical distribution widely used in practice to evaluate the *sample mean* when the *population standard deviation* is estimated from the data. Also known as Student's distribution. It is similar in shape to the *normal distribution* with slightly longer tails. See *t-test*. See Table 2.[17]

Testing   A means of determining the ability of an item to meet specified requirements by subjecting the item to a set of physical, chemical, environmental, or operating actions and conditions.[6]

Tests for means   See *means, tests for.*

Tests for proportions   See *proportions, tests for.*

Tests for regression coefficients   See *regression coefficients, tests for.*

Tests for significance   See *significance, tests for.*

Test for variances   See *variances, tests for.*

Third quartile (Q_3 or upper quartile) The portion of a distribution where one quarter of the data lies above it. See *quartiles.*[30]

Threshold control
See Part II—Control
Chart Guide
Threshold control applies to *process control* where the primary interest is in events near *control limits.* Typical *control charts* used for this purpose are *h, g, c, u, np, p, x* (individuals), MR, $\bar{x}$, *R,* and *s* charts. This type of control is most often used in the early stages of a quality improvement process. See also *deviation control.*[11]

Tightened inspection An *inspection* more severe than *normal inspection,* to which the latter is switched when inspection results of a predetermined number of *lots* indicate that the quality level achieved by the *process* is poorer than that specified.[18]

Time series The sequence of successive time intervals.[30]

Tolerance The difference between upper and lower *specification limits.*[18]

Tolerance limit See *specification limit.*

Transformation A reexpression of data aimed toward achieving *normality.*[30]

Treatment The specific setting of *factor levels* for an *experimental unit.*[19]

Trimodal A *probability distribution* having three distinct statistical modes.[30]

True value   A value for a *quantitative characteristic* that does not contain any sampling or measurement variability. (The true value is never exactly known; it is a hypothetical concept.)[11]

t-test   A *test for significance* that uses the *t distribution* to compare a *sample statistic* to a hypothesized *population mean* or to compare two means. See *t*-test (one sample), *t*-test (two-sample), *t*-test (paired data).

Note: Testing the equality of the means of two normal populations with unknown but equal variances can be extended to the comparison of *k* population means. This test procedure is called *analysis of variance (ANOVA).*[17]

t-test (one-sample) $$t = \frac{\bar{x} - \mu_0}{s / \sqrt{n}}$$

where $\bar{x}$ is the mean of the data, μ_0 is the hypothesized *population mean,* s is the *sample standard deviation,* and n is the *sample* size. The degrees of freedom are $n - 1$.[16]

t-test (paired data)   Samples are paired to eliminate differences between specimens. The test could involve two machines, two test methods, two treatments, and so on. Observations are the pairs of the two machines, tests, treatments, and so on. The differences of the pairs of observations on each of the *n* specimens: $d_j = x_{1j} - x_{2j}$, $j = 1, 2, \ldots n,$

$$t = \frac{\bar{d}}{s_d / \sqrt{n}}$$

where $\bar{d} = \frac{1}{n}\sum_{j=1}^{n} d_j$

$$\text{and } s_d^2 = \frac{\sum_{j=1}^{n} d_j^2 - \frac{\left(\sum_{j=1}^{n} d_j\right)^2}{n}}{n-1} \, .^{26}$$

t-test (two-sample)
Equal variances

When there are two *populations* with unknown *means* and unknown *variances* that are assumed to be equal, the variances can be pooled to determine a pooled variance:

$$s_p^2 = \frac{(n_1 - 1)s_1^2 + (n_2 - 1)s_2^2}{n_1 + n_2 - 2}$$

where s_1 and s_2 are the individual sample variances and n_1 and n_2 are the respective *sample sizes.*

The *t*-test is:

$$t = \frac{\bar{x}_1 - \bar{x}_2}{s_p \sqrt{\frac{1}{n_1} + \frac{1}{n_2}}}$$

where s_p is the pooled variance calculated above, $\bar{x}_1$ and $\bar{x}_2$ are the means of the respective populations, and n_1 and n_2 are the respective *sample* sizes.

The degrees of freedom, v: $v = n_1 + n_2 - 2.$

Unequal variances

When there are two *populations* with unknown *means* and unknown variances that are assumed to be unequal, the sample standard deviation of $(\bar{x}_1 - \bar{x}_2)$ is:

$$s = \sqrt{\frac{s_1^2}{n_1} + \frac{s_2^2}{n_2}}$$

The degrees of freedom are:

$$v = \frac{\left(s_1^2 / n_1 + s_2^2 / n_2\right)^2}{\left[\left(s_1^2 / n_1\right)^2 / (n_1 - 1)\right] + \left[\left(s_2^2 / n_2\right)^2 / (n_2 - 1)\right]} - 2 \, .^{26}$$

Two-tailed test   A *hypothesis* test that involves tails of a distribution. Example: We wish to reject the *null hypothesis*, H_0, if the true *mean* is within minimum and maximum (two tails) limits.[26]

$$H_0: \mu = \mu_0$$

$$H_1: \mu \neq \mu_0$$

Type I error   The *probability* or risk of rejecting a *hypothesis* that is true. This probability is represented by α *(alpha)*.

See diagram below. See *operating characteristic curve* and *producer's risk.*[12]

Type II error   The *probability* or risk of accepting a *hypothesis* that is false. This probability is represented by β *(beta)*.

See diagram below. See *power curve* and *consumer's risk.*[12]

	H_0 True	H_0 False
Do not reject H_0	**Correct decision**	**Error** Type II
Reject H_0	**Error** Type I	**Correct decision**

U

_u_ (count per unit) The *events* or events per *unit* where the opportunity is variable. More than one event may occur in a unit.

Note: For *u*, the opportunity is variable; for *c*, the opportunity for occurrence is fixed.[4]

_u_ chart
See Part II—Control
Chart Guide

An *attribute control chart* for number of *events* per unit where the opportunity is variable.

Note: Events of a particular type, for example, number of absentees or number of sales leads, form the count. In the quality field, events are often expressed as nonconformities and the variable opportunity relates to *subgroups* of variable size or variable amounts of material.

Central line: $\bar{u}$.

Control limits: $\bar{u} \pm 3\sqrt{\bar{u}/n}$

where $\bar{u}$ is the average number of events per unit and *n* is the total number of samples. $\bar{u}$ is calculated as $\bar{u} = \bar{c}/n$.

Note: If the *lower control limit (LCL)* calculates ≤ 0 there is no LCL.[12, 18]

U See *upper specification limit.*

UCL See *upper control limit.*

Unacceptable quality See *limiting quality level.*[4]
level (UQL)

Uncertainty A *parameter* that characterizes the *dispersion* of the values that could reasonably be attributed to the particular quantity subject to measurement or *characteristic*. Uncertainty indicates the variability of the measured value or characteristic that considers two major components of error: (1) *bias* and (2) the random error from the *imprecision* of the measurement process.[15, 18]

Unique lot A *lot* formed under conditions peculiar to that lot and not part of a routine sequence.[18]

Unit A quantity of product, material, or service forming a cohesive entity on which a measurement or observation can be made.[4]

Universe A group of *populations,* often reflecting different *characteristics* of the items or material under consideration.[15]

Upper control limit The *control limit* on a *control chart* that
(UCL) defines the upper control boundary.[18]

Upper quartile See *third quartile.*

Upper specification limit or upper tolerance limit (U)   The *specification limit* that defines the upper limiting value.[18]

UQL   See *limiting quality level.*

URPL   See *rejectable process level.*

Variable (control chart usage) A quality *characteristic* that is from a *continuous scale* and is *quantitative* in nature.[30]

Variables control chart A *Shewhart control chart* where the measure plotted represents data on a *continuous scale*.[18]

Variables, inspection by See *inspection by variables*.

Variance A measure of the *variation* in the data. When working with the entire *population*, the population variance is used; when working with a *sample*, the sample variance is used. The population variance is based on the mean of the squared deviations from the *arithmetic mean* and is given by

$$\sigma^2 = \frac{1}{n}\sum(x - \mu)^2$$

The sample variance is based on the squared deviations from the *arithmetic mean* divided by n – 1 and is given by

$$s^2 = \frac{1}{n-1}\sum(x - \bar{x})^2$$

where n is the number of data points in the sample or population, μ is the *population mean*, x is the *observed value* of the quality characteristic, and $\bar{x}$ is the sample mean. See *standard deviation*.[30]

Variances, tests for   A formal statistical test based on the *null hypothesis* that the *variances* of different groups are equal. Many times in *regression analysis* a formal test of variances is not done. Instead, *residual analysis* checks the assumption of equal variance across the values of the *response variable* in the *model*. For two variances, see *F-test*.[30]

Variation   The difference between values of a *characteristic*. Variation can be measured and calculated in different ways, such as *range, standard deviation,* or *variance.* Also known as *dispersion* or *spread.*[18]

W

w The span of the *moving average*.[30]

w_t The *exponentially weighted moving average (EWMA)* at the present time t.[30]

w_{t-1} The *exponentially weighted moving average (EWMA)* at the immediately preceding time interval.[30]

Warning limits   There is a high *probability* that the *statistic* under consideration is in a *state of statistical control* when it is within the warning limits (generally 2σ) of a *control chart*. See *Shewhart control limits*.

Note: When the value of the statistic plotted lies outside a warning limit but within the *action limit*, increased supervision of the *process* to prespecified rules is generally required.[18]

X

χ^2 **distribution**
(pronounced chi-square)
A positively skewed distribution that varies with the *degrees of freedom* with a minimum value of 0. See Table 4.[30]

χ^2 **statistic**
A value obtained from the χ^2 *distribution* at a given percentage point and a given *degree of freedom*.[30]

χ^2 **test**
A *statistic* used in testing a *hypothesis* concerning the discrepancy between *observed* and expected results. See Table 4.[30]

x
The observed value of a quality characteristic; specific observed values are designated x_1, x_2, x_3, and so on. x is also used as a predictor value. See *input* or *predictor variable*.[8]

$\bar{x}$ (pronounced *X*-bar)
The *average,* or *arithmetic mean.* The average of a set of n observed values is the sum of the observed values divided by n:

$$\bar{x} = \frac{x_1 + x_2 + \ldots + x_n}{n} \quad .[5]$$

$\bar{x}_0$
See *control chart, standard given.*

$\bar{x}_i$ The average of the ith subgroup (when $n = 1$, $\bar{x}_i = x = x_i$).[12]

$\bar{\bar{x}}$ (pronounced X-double bar)   The average for the set under consideration of the subgroup values of $\bar{x}$.[12]

x **chart**   See *individuals chart.*

$\bar{x}$ **chart (average control chart)** See Part II—Control Chart Guide

A *variables control chart* for evaluating the *process* level in terms of *subgroup averages.*

Central line: $\bar{\bar{x}}$ (if standard given, $\bar{x}_0$)

Control limits: $\bar{\bar{x}} \pm A_3\bar{s}$ or $\bar{\bar{x}} \pm A_2\bar{R}$

(if standard given, $\bar{x}_0 \pm A\sigma_0$ or $\bar{x}_0 \pm A_2R_0$)

where $\bar{\bar{x}}$ is the average of the subgroup values; $\bar{s}$ is the sample *standard deviation;* A, A_2, and A_3 are *control chart factors* (see Table 5); σ_0 is the standard value of the population standard deviation; and R_0 is the standard value of the *range.* (Use the formula with $\bar{R}$ when the sample size is small; the formula with $\bar{s}$ when the sample is larger—generally >10 to 12.)[8, 11, 12, 18]

y y is sometimes used as an alternate to x as an observation. In such cases, y_0, and should be substituted where appropriate. See *output* or *response variable*.[14]

$\bar{y}$ (pronounced y-bar)   The *average,* or *arithmetic mean,* of y. It is calculated exactly the same as $\bar{x}$.[30]

$\bar{\bar{y}}$ (pronounced y-double-bar)   The average for the set under consideration of the subgroup values of $\bar{y}$. See y.[12]

$\bar{y}_0$ See y and *control charts, standard given.*

z-confidence interval for means (one-sample)

Given an unknown *mean* μ and known *variance* σ^2, then the $100(1 - \alpha)\%$ *two-sided* confidence interval on μ is:

$$\bar{x} - Z_{\alpha/2}\frac{\sigma}{\sqrt{n}} \le \mu \le \bar{x} + Z_{\alpha/2}\frac{\sigma}{\sqrt{n}}$$

where $\bar{x}$ is the *mean* of the data, σ is the *population standard deviation*, n is the *sample* size.[26]

z-test (one-sample)

Given an unknown *mean* μ, and known *variance* σ^2:

$$z = \frac{\bar{x} - \mu_0}{\sigma / \sqrt{n}}$$

where $\bar{x}$ is the mean of the data, μ_0 is the standard value of the *population mean*, σ is the *population standard deviation*, and n is the *sample* size.

Note: If the variance is unknown, then the *t-test* applies.[26]

z-test (two proportions)

To test if two binomial parameters are equal, the null hypothesis is H_0: $p_1 = p_2$ and the alternate hypothesis is H_1: $p_1 \ne p_2$. If the null hypothesis is true, then $p_1 = p_2 = p$, and

$$\hat{p} = \frac{n_1 \hat{p}_1 + n_2 \hat{p}_2}{n_1 + n_2}$$

The test is then:

$$z = \frac{\hat{p}_1 - \hat{p}_2}{\sqrt{\hat{p}(1 - \hat{p}) \left(\dfrac{1}{n_1} + \dfrac{1}{n_2} \right)}}$$

and H_0 should be rejected if $|z| > z_{\alpha/2}$.[26]

z-test (two-sample)   Given unknown *means* μ_1 and μ_2, and known *variances* σ_1^2 and σ_2^2:

$$z = \frac{\bar{x}_1 - \bar{x}_2}{\sqrt{\dfrac{\sigma_1^2}{n_1} + \dfrac{\sigma_2^2}{n_2}}}$$

where $\bar{x}_1$ is the mean of the first *population* and $\bar{x}_2$ is the mean of the second population; σ_1 is the *standard deviation* of the first population and σ_2 is the standard deviation of the second population; and n_1 and n_2 are the respective *sample* sizes.

Note: If the variance is unknown, then the *t-test* applies.[26]

Z

II

Control Chart Guide

This control chart guide is a graphical summary of the control charts defined in this book. It is designed as an aid in selecting the appropriate control chart to use in various applications.[10]

Note: The reader should verify any selection by using the references associated with the particular control chart selected.

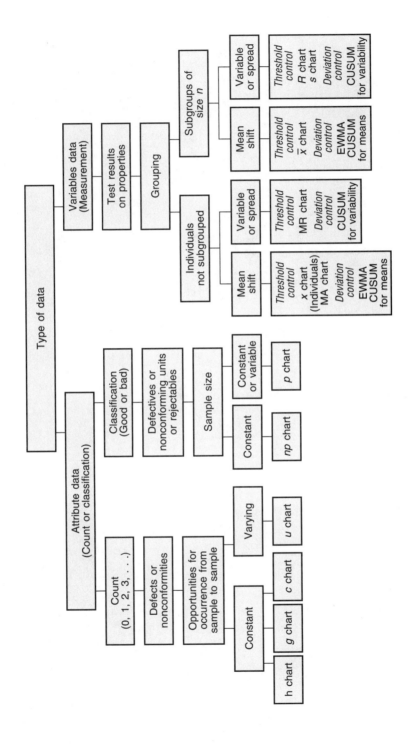

129

III

Statistical Tables

Table 1A   Areas under the normal curve from $Z = -4.009$ to 3.500.

The proportion of total area (α) under the curve that is under the portion of the curve from $-\infty$ to $\frac{x-\mu}{\sigma}$ (x represents any desired value of the variable x). Note: entries must be multiplied by 10^{-3}.

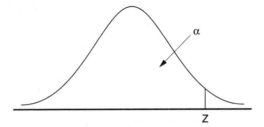

$\frac{x-\mu}{\sigma}$	0.009	0.008	0.007	0.006	0.005	0.004	0.003	0.002	0.001	0.000
−4.00	0.03049	0.03062	0.03075	0.03088	0.03101	0.03114	0.03127	0.03140	0.03154	0.03167
−3.99	0.03181	0.03194	0.03208	0.03221	0.03235	0.03248	0.03262	0.03276	0.03290	0.03304
−3.98	0.03318	0.03332	0.03346	0.03360	0.03374	0.03388	0.03403	0.03417	0.03431	0.03446
−3.97	0.03460	0.03475	0.03490	0.03504	0.03519	0.03534	0.03549	0.03564	0.03579	0.03594
−3.96	0.03609	0.03624	0.03639	0.03654	0.03670	0.03685	0.03701	0.03716	0.03732	0.03747
−3.95	0.03763	0.03779	0.03795	0.03811	0.03827	0.03843	0.03859	0.03875	0.03891	0.03908
−3.94	0.03924	0.03940	0.03957	0.03973	0.03990	0.04007	0.04023	0.04040	0.04057	0.04074
−3.93	0.04091	0.04108	0.04125	0.04143	0.04160	0.04177	0.04195	0.04212	0.04230	0.04247
−3.92	0.04265	0.04283	0.04301	0.04319	0.04336	0.04355	0.04373	0.04391	0.04409	0.04427
−3.91	0.04446	0.04464	0.04483	0.04502	0.04520	0.04539	0.04558	0.04577	0.04596	0.04615
−3.90	0.04634	0.04653	0.04672	0.04692	0.04711	0.04731	0.04750	0.04770	0.04790	0.04810
−3.89	0.04830	0.04850	0.04870	0.04890	0.04910	0.04930	0.04951	0.04971	0.04992	0.05012
−3.88	0.05033	0.05054	0.05075	0.05095	0.05116	0.05138	0.05159	0.05180	0.05201	0.05223
−3.87	0.05244	0.05266	0.05288	0.05309	0.05331	0.05353	0.05375	0.05397	0.05419	0.05442
−3.86	0.05464	0.05487	0.05509	0.05532	0.05554	0.05577	0.05600	0.05623	0.05646	0.05669
−3.85	0.05693	0.05716	0.05739	0.05763	0.05786	0.05810	0.05834	0.05858	0.05882	0.05906
−3.84	0.05930	0.05954	0.05979	0.06003	0.06028	0.06052	0.06077	0.06102	0.06127	0.06152
−3.83	0.06177	0.06202	0.06227	0.06253	0.06278	0.06304	0.06329	0.06355	0.06381	0.06407
−3.82	0.06433	0.06459	0.06486	0.06512	0.06539	0.06565	0.06592	0.06619	0.06646	0.06673
−3.81	0.06700	0.06727	0.06754	0.06782	0.06809	0.06837	0.06865	0.06892	0.06920	0.06948
−3.80	0.06976	0.07005	0.07033	0.07062	0.07090	0.07119	0.07148	0.07177	0.07206	0.07235
−3.79	0.07264	0.07293	0.07323	0.07352	0.07382	0.07412	0.07442	0.07472	0.07502	0.07532
−3.78	0.07563	0.07593	0.07624	0.07655	0.07685	0.07716	0.07747	0.07779	0.07810	0.07841
−3.77	0.07873	0.07905	0.07936	0.07968	0.08000	0.08033	0.08065	0.08097	0.08130	0.08162
−3.76	0.08195	0.08228	0.08261	0.08294	0.08327	0.08361	0.08394	0.08428	0.08462	0.08496
−3.75	0.08530	0.08564	0.08598	0.08633	0.08667	0.08702	0.08737	0.08771	0.08807	0.08842
−3.74	0.08877	0.08913	0.08948	0.08984	0.09020	0.09056	0.09092	0.09128	0.09164	0.09201

continued

continued

$\frac{x-\mu}{\sigma}$	0.009	0.008	0.007	0.006	0.005	0.004	0.003	0.002	0.001	0.000
−3.73	0.09238	0.09274	0.09311	0.09349	0.09386	0.09423	0.09461	0.09498	0.09536	0.09574
−3.72	0.09612	0.09650	0.09689	0.09727	0.09766	0.09805	0.09843	0.09883	0.09922	0.09961
−3.71	0.10001	0.10040	0.10080	0.10120	0.10160	0.10200	0.10241	0.10281	0.10322	0.10363
−3.70	0.10404	0.10445	0.10486	0.10528	0.10570	0.10611	0.10653	0.10695	0.10738	0.10780
−3.69	0.10823	0.10865	0.10908	0.10951	0.10994	0.11038	0.11081	0.11125	0.11169	0.11213
−3.68	0.11257	0.11301	0.11346	0.11390	0.11435	0.11480	0.11525	0.11571	0.11616	0.11662
−3.67	0.11708	0.11753	0.11800	0.11846	0.11892	0.11939	0.11986	0.12033	0.12080	0.12128
−3.66	0.12175	0.12223	0.12271	0.12319	0.12367	0.12415	0.12464	0.12513	0.12562	0.12611
−3.65	0.12660	0.12710	0.12759	0.12809	0.12859	0.12909	0.12960	0.13010	0.13061	0.13112
−3.64	0.13163	0.13214	0.13266	0.13318	0.13370	0.13422	0.13474	0.13526	0.13579	0.13632
−3.63	0.13685	0.13738	0.13792	0.13845	0.13899	0.13953	0.14007	0.14062	0.14116	0.14171
−3.62	0.14226	0.14281	0.14337	0.14392	0.14448	0.14504	0.14560	0.14617	0.14673	0.14730
−3.61	0.14787	0.14844	0.14902	0.14960	0.15017	0.15075	0.15134	0.15192	0.15251	0.15310
−3.60	0.15369	0.15428	0.15488	0.15548	0.15608	0.15668	0.15728	0.15789	0.15850	0.15911
−3.59	0.15972	0.16034	0.16095	0.16157	0.16220	0.16282	0.16345	0.16407	0.16471	0.16534
−3.58	0.16597	0.16661	0.16725	0.16789	0.16854	0.16919	0.16984	0.17049	0.17114	0.17180
−3.57	0.17246	0.17312	0.17378	0.17445	0.17511	0.17578	0.17646	0.17713	0.17781	0.17849
−3.56	0.17917	0.17986	0.18055	0.18124	0.18193	0.18262	0.18332	0.18402	0.18472	0.18543
−3.55	0.18613	0.18684	0.18756	0.18827	0.18899	0.18971	0.19043	0.19116	0.19189	0.19262
−3.54	0.19335	0.19408	0.19482	0.19556	0.19631	0.19705	0.19780	0.19855	0.19931	0.20006
−3.53	0.20082	0.20159	0.20235	0.20312	0.20389	0.20466	0.20544	0.20621	0.20700	0.20778
−3.52	0.20857	0.20936	0.21015	0.21094	0.21174	0.21254	0.21335	0.21415	0.21496	0.21577
−3.51	0.21659	0.21741	0.21823	0.21905	0.21988	0.22071	0.22154	0.22237	0.22321	0.22405
−3.50	0.22490	0.22574	0.22659	0.22745	0.22830	0.22916	0.23002	0.23089	0.23176	0.23263

Table 1B   Areas under the normal curve from $Z = -3.500$ to -3.000.

The proportion of total area (α) under the curve that is under the portion of the curve from $-\infty$ to $\frac{x-\mu}{\sigma}$ (x represents any desired value of the variable x). Note: entries must be multiplied by 10^{-2}.

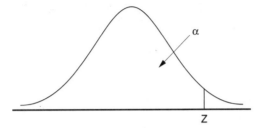

$\frac{x-\mu}{\sigma}$	0.009	0.008	0.007	0.006	0.005	0.004	0.003	0.002	0.001	0.000
-3.50	0.02249	0.02257	0.02266	0.02274	0.02283	0.02292	0.02300	0.02309	0.02318	0.02326
-3.49	0.02335	0.02344	0.02353	0.02361	0.02370	0.02379	0.02388	0.02397	0.02406	0.02415
-3.48	0.02424	0.02433	0.02442	0.02452	0.02461	0.02470	0.02479	0.02488	0.02498	0.02507
-3.47	0.02516	0.02526	0.02535	0.02545	0.02554	0.02564	0.02573	0.02583	0.02593	0.02602
-3.46	0.02612	0.02622	0.02632	0.02641	0.02651	0.02661	0.02671	0.02681	0.02691	0.02701
-3.45	0.02711	0.02721	0.02731	0.02741	0.02751	0.02762	0.02772	0.02782	0.02793	0.02803
-3.44	0.02813	0.02824	0.02834	0.02845	0.02855	0.02866	0.02876	0.02887	0.02898	0.02909
-3.43	0.02919	0.02930	0.02941	0.02952	0.02963	0.02974	0.02985	0.02996	0.03007	0.03018
-3.42	0.03029	0.03040	0.03051	0.03063	0.03074	0.03085	0.03097	0.03108	0.03120	0.03131
-3.41	0.03143	0.03154	0.03166	0.03177	0.03189	0.03201	0.03213	0.03224	0.03236	0.03248
-3.40	0.03260	0.03272	0.03284	0.03296	0.03308	0.03320	0.03333	0.03345	0.03357	0.03369
-3.39	0.03382	0.03394	0.03406	0.03419	0.03431	0.03444	0.03457	0.03469	0.03482	0.03495
-3.38	0.03507	0.03520	0.03533	0.03546	0.03559	0.03572	0.03585	0.03598	0.03611	0.03624
-3.37	0.03638	0.03651	0.03664	0.03677	0.03691	0.03704	0.03718	0.03731	0.03745	0.03758
-3.36	0.03772	0.03786	0.03800	0.03813	0.03827	0.03841	0.03855	0.03869	0.03883	0.03897
-3.35	0.03911	0.03925	0.03940	0.03954	0.03968	0.03983	0.03997	0.04012	0.04026	0.04041
-3.34	0.04055	0.04070	0.04085	0.04099	0.04114	0.04129	0.04144	0.04159	0.04174	0.04189
-3.33	0.04204	0.04219	0.04234	0.04250	0.04265	0.04280	0.04296	0.04311	0.04327	0.04342
-3.32	0.04358	0.04374	0.04389	0.04405	0.04421	0.04437	0.04453	0.04469	0.04485	0.04501
-3.31	0.04517	0.04533	0.04549	0.04566	0.04582	0.04599	0.04615	0.04632	0.04648	0.04665
-3.30	0.04681	0.04698	0.04715	0.04732	0.04749	0.04766	0.04783	0.04800	0.04817	0.04834
-3.29	0.04851	0.04869	0.04886	0.04904	0.04921	0.04939	0.04956	0.04974	0.04992	0.05009
-3.28	0.05027	0.05045	0.05063	0.05081	0.05099	0.05117	0.05135	0.05154	0.05172	0.05190
-3.27	0.05209	0.05227	0.05246	0.05264	0.05283	0.05302	0.05321	0.05339	0.05358	0.05377
-3.26	0.05396	0.05416	0.05435	0.05454	0.05473	0.05493	0.05512	0.05531	0.05551	0.05571
-3.25	0.05590	0.05610	0.05630	0.05650	0.05670	0.05690	0.05710	0.05730	0.05750	0.05770
-3.24	0.05791	0.05811	0.05831	0.05852	0.05873	0.05893	0.05914	0.05935	0.05956	0.05976

continued

continued

$\dfrac{x-\mu}{\sigma}$	0.009	0.008	0.007	0.006	0.005	0.004	0.003	0.002	0.001	0.000
-3.23	0.05997	0.06019	0.06040	0.06061	0.06082	0.06103	0.06125	0.06146	0.06168	0.06190
-3.22	0.06211	0.06233	0.06255	0.06277	0.06299	0.06321	0.06343	0.06365	0.06387	0.06410
-3.21	0.06432	0.06454	0.06477	0.06500	0.06522	0.06545	0.06568	0.06591	0.06614	0.06637
-3.20	0.06660	0.06683	0.06706	0.06730	0.06753	0.06777	0.06800	0.06824	0.06848	0.06871
-3.19	0.06895	0.06919	0.06943	0.06967	0.06992	0.07016	0.07040	0.07065	0.07089	0.07114
-3.18	0.07138	0.07163	0.07188	0.07213	0.07238	0.07263	0.07288	0.07313	0.07338	0.07364
-3.17	0.07389	0.07415	0.07440	0.07466	0.07492	0.07518	0.07544	0.07570	0.07596	0.07622
-3.16	0.07648	0.07675	0.07701	0.07728	0.07754	0.07781	0.07808	0.07834	0.07861	0.07888
-3.15	0.07916	0.07943	0.07970	0.07997	0.08025	0.08052	0.08080	0.08108	0.08136	0.08164
-3.14	0.08192	0.08220	0.08248	0.08276	0.08304	0.08333	0.08361	0.08390	0.08419	0.08447
-3.13	0.08476	0.08505	0.08534	0.08563	0.08593	0.08622	0.08651	0.08681	0.08711	0.08740
-3.12	0.08770	0.08800	0.08830	0.08860	0.08890	0.08921	0.08951	0.08981	0.09012	0.09043
-3.11	0.09073	0.09104	0.09135	0.09166	0.09197	0.09228	0.09260	0.09291	0.09323	0.09354
-3.10	0.09386	0.09418	0.09450	0.09482	0.09514	0.09546	0.09578	0.09611	0.09643	0.09676
-3.09	0.09709	0.09742	0.09774	0.09808	0.09841	0.09874	0.09907	0.09941	0.09974	0.10008
-3.08	0.10042	0.10075	0.10109	0.10143	0.10178	0.10212	0.10246	0.10281	0.10315	0.10350
-3.07	0.10385	0.10420	0.10455	0.10490	0.10525	0.10560	0.10596	0.10631	0.10667	0.10703
-3.06	0.10739	0.10775	0.10811	0.10847	0.10883	0.10920	0.10957	0.10993	0.11030	0.11067
-3.05	0.11104	0.11141	0.11178	0.11216	0.11253	0.11291	0.11328	0.11366	0.11404	0.11442
-3.04	0.11480	0.11518	0.11557	0.11595	0.11634	0.11673	0.11712	0.11751	0.11790	0.11829
-3.03	0.11868	0.11908	0.11947	0.11987	0.12027	0.12067	0.12107	0.12147	0.12187	0.12228
-3.02	0.12268	0.12309	0.12350	0.12391	0.12432	0.12473	0.12514	0.12556	0.12597	0.12639
-3.01	0.12681	0.12722	0.12764	0.12807	0.12849	0.12891	0.12934	0.12977	0.13019	0.13062
-3.00	0.13105	0.13149	0.13192	0.13235	0.13279	0.13323	0.13367	0.13411	0.13455	0.13499

Table 1C Areas under the normal curve from $Z = -3.000$ to -2.500.

The proportion of total area (α) under the curve that is under the portion of the curve from $-\infty$ to $\frac{x-\mu}{\sigma}$ (x represents any desired value of the variable x). Note: entries must be multiplied by 10^{-2}.

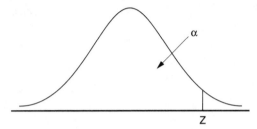

$\frac{x-\mu}{\sigma}$	0.009	0.008	0.007	0.006	0.005	0.004	0.003	0.002	0.001	0.000
-3.00	0.13105	0.13149	0.13192	0.13235	0.13279	0.13323	0.13367	0.13411	0.13455	0.13499
-2.99	0.13543	0.13588	0.13633	0.13677	0.13722	0.13767	0.13812	0.13858	0.13903	0.13949
-2.98	0.13995	0.14040	0.14086	0.14133	0.14179	0.14225	0.14272	0.14319	0.14365	0.14412
-2.97	0.14460	0.14507	0.14554	0.14602	0.14649	0.14697	0.14745	0.14793	0.14842	0.14890
-2.96	0.14939	0.14987	0.15036	0.15085	0.15134	0.15183	0.15233	0.15282	0.15332	0.15382
-2.95	0.15432	0.15482	0.15532	0.15583	0.15633	0.15684	0.15735	0.15786	0.15837	0.15889
-2.94	0.15940	0.15992	0.16044	0.16096	0.16148	0.16200	0.16252	0.16305	0.16358	0.16411
-2.93	0.16464	0.16517	0.16570	0.16624	0.16677	0.16731	0.16785	0.16839	0.16894	0.16948
-2.92	0.17003	0.17058	0.17112	0.17168	0.17223	0.17278	0.17334	0.17390	0.17445	0.17502
-2.91	0.17558	0.17614	0.17671	0.17728	0.17784	0.17841	0.17899	0.17956	0.18014	0.18071
-2.90	0.18129	0.18187	0.18246	0.18304	0.18363	0.18421	0.18480	0.18539	0.18599	0.18658
-2.89	0.18718	0.18778	0.18837	0.18898	0.18958	0.19018	0.19079	0.19140	0.19201	0.19262
-2.88	0.19323	0.19385	0.19447	0.19509	0.19571	0.19633	0.19695	0.19758	0.19821	0.19884
-2.87	0.19947	0.20010	0.20074	0.20137	0.20201	0.20265	0.20330	0.20394	0.20459	0.20524
-2.86	0.20589	0.20654	0.20719	0.20785	0.20850	0.20916	0.20983	0.21049	0.21115	0.21182
-2.85	0.21249	0.21316	0.21383	0.21451	0.21518	0.21586	0.21654	0.21723	0.21791	0.21860
-2.84	0.21928	0.21997	0.22067	0.22136	0.22206	0.22276	0.22346	0.22416	0.22486	0.22557
-2.83	0.22628	0.22699	0.22770	0.22841	0.22913	0.22985	0.23057	0.23129	0.23201	0.23274
-2.82	0.23347	0.23420	0.23493	0.23567	0.23640	0.23714	0.23788	0.23863	0.23937	0.24012
-2.81	0.24087	0.24162	0.24237	0.24313	0.24389	0.24465	0.24541	0.24617	0.24694	0.24771
-2.80	0.24848	0.24925	0.25003	0.25080	0.25158	0.25236	0.25315	0.25393	0.25472	0.25551
-2.79	0.25631	0.25710	0.25790	0.25870	0.25950	0.26030	0.26111	0.26192	0.26273	0.26354
-2.78	0.26436	0.26517	0.26599	0.26681	0.26764	0.26847	0.26929	0.27013	0.27096	0.27179
-2.77	0.27263	0.27347	0.27432	0.27516	0.27601	0.27686	0.27771	0.27857	0.27942	0.28028
-2.76	0.28114	0.28201	0.28287	0.28374	0.28461	0.28549	0.28636	0.28724	0.28812	0.28901
-2.75	0.28989	0.29078	0.29167	0.29256	0.29346	0.29436	0.29526	0.29616	0.29707	0.29798
-2.74	0.29889	0.29980	0.30072	0.30163	0.30255	0.30348	0.30440	0.30533	0.30626	0.30720

continued

continued

$\frac{x-\mu}{\sigma}$	0.009	0.008	0.007	0.006	0.005	0.004	0.003	0.002	0.001	0.000
-2.73	0.30813	0.30907	0.31001	0.31096	0.31190	0.31285	0.31380	0.31476	0.31571	0.31667
-2.72	0.31763	0.31860	0.31957	0.32053	0.32151	0.32248	0.32346	0.32444	0.32542	0.32641
-2.71	0.32740	0.32839	0.32938	0.33038	0.33138	0.33238	0.33339	0.33439	0.33540	0.33642
-2.70	0.33743	0.33845	0.33947	0.34050	0.34152	0.34255	0.34358	0.34462	0.34566	0.34670
-2.69	0.34774	0.34879	0.34984	0.35089	0.35194	0.35300	0.35406	0.35512	0.35619	0.35726
-2.68	0.35833	0.35941	0.36048	0.36157	0.36265	0.36374	0.36482	0.36592	0.36701	0.36811
-2.67	0.36921	0.37032	0.37142	0.37253	0.37365	0.37476	0.37588	0.37700	0.37813	0.37926
-2.66	0.38039	0.38152	0.38266	0.38380	0.38494	0.38609	0.38724	0.38839	0.38954	0.39070
-2.65	0.39186	0.39303	0.39420	0.39537	0.39654	0.39772	0.39890	0.40008	0.40127	0.40246
-2.64	0.40365	0.40485	0.40605	0.40725	0.40845	0.40966	0.41088	0.41209	0.41331	0.41453
-2.63	0.41575	0.41698	0.41821	0.41945	0.42069	0.42193	0.42317	0.42442	0.42567	0.42692
-2.62	0.42818	0.42944	0.43071	0.43197	0.43324	0.43452	0.43580	0.43708	0.43836	0.43965
-2.61	0.44094	0.44223	0.44353	0.44483	0.44614	0.44745	0.44876	0.45007	0.45139	0.45271
-2.60	0.45404	0.45536	0.45670	0.45803	0.45937	0.46071	0.46206	0.46341	0.46476	0.46612
-2.59	0.46748	0.46884	0.47021	0.47158	0.47295	0.47433	0.47571	0.47710	0.47849	0.47988
-2.58	0.48128	0.48267	0.48408	0.48548	0.48689	0.48831	0.48973	0.49115	0.49257	0.49400
-2.57	0.49543	0.49687	0.49831	0.49975	0.50120	0.50265	0.50411	0.50556	0.50703	0.50849
-2.56	0.50996	0.51144	0.51291	0.51439	0.51588	0.51737	0.51886	0.52036	0.52186	0.52336
-2.55	0.52487	0.52638	0.52790	0.52942	0.53094	0.53247	0.53400	0.53553	0.53707	0.53861
-2.54	0.54016	0.54171	0.54327	0.54483	0.54639	0.54796	0.54953	0.55110	0.55268	0.55426
-2.53	0.55585	0.55744	0.55903	0.56063	0.56224	0.56384	0.56545	0.56707	0.56869	0.57031
-2.52	0.57194	0.57357	0.57521	0.57685	0.57849	0.58014	0.58179	0.58345	0.58511	0.58677
-2.51	0.58844	0.59012	0.59179	0.59348	0.59516	0.59685	0.59855	0.60025	0.60195	0.60366
-2.50	0.60537	0.60708	0.60880	0.61053	0.61226	0.61399	0.61573	0.61747	0.61922	0.62097

Table 1D Areas under the normal curve from $Z = -2.500$ to -2.000.

The proportion of total area (α) under the curve that is under the portion of the curve from $-\infty$ to $\frac{x-\mu}{\sigma}$ (x represents any desired value of the variable x). Note: entries must be multiplied by 10^{-1}.

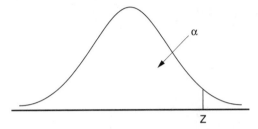

$\frac{x-\mu}{\sigma}$	0.009	0.008	0.007	0.006	0.005	0.004	0.003	0.002	0.001	0.000
-2.50	0.06054	0.06071	0.06088	0.06105	0.06123	0.06140	0.06157	0.06175	0.06192	0.06210
-2.49	0.06227	0.06245	0.06262	0.06280	0.06298	0.06316	0.06333	0.06351	0.06369	0.06387
-2.48	0.06405	0.06423	0.06441	0.06459	0.06478	0.06496	0.06514	0.06532	0.06551	0.06569
-2.47	0.06588	0.06606	0.06625	0.06643	0.06662	0.06680	0.06699	0.06718	0.06737	0.06756
-2.46	0.06775	0.06794	0.06813	0.06832	0.06851	0.06870	0.06889	0.06908	0.06928	0.06947
-2.45	0.06966	0.06986	0.07005	0.07025	0.07044	0.07064	0.07084	0.07103	0.07123	0.07143
-2.44	0.07163	0.07183	0.07203	0.07223	0.07243	0.07263	0.07283	0.07303	0.07323	0.07344
-2.43	0.07364	0.07384	0.07405	0.07425	0.07446	0.07466	0.07487	0.07508	0.07529	0.07549
-2.42	0.07570	0.07591	0.07612	0.07633	0.07654	0.07675	0.07696	0.07718	0.07739	0.07760
-2.41	0.07782	0.07803	0.07825	0.07846	0.07868	0.07889	0.07911	0.07933	0.07954	0.07976
-2.40	0.07998	0.08020	0.08042	0.08064	0.08086	0.08108	0.08131	0.08153	0.08175	0.08198
-2.39	0.08220	0.08242	0.08265	0.08288	0.08310	0.08333	0.08356	0.08378	0.08401	0.08424
-2.38	0.08447	0.08470	0.08493	0.08516	0.08540	0.08563	0.08586	0.08609	0.08633	0.08656
-2.37	0.08680	0.08703	0.08727	0.08751	0.08774	0.08798	0.08822	0.08846	0.08870	0.08894
-2.36	0.08918	0.08942	0.08966	0.08991	0.09015	0.09039	0.09064	0.09088	0.09113	0.09137
-2.35	0.09162	0.09187	0.09212	0.09236	0.09261	0.09286	0.09311	0.09336	0.09362	0.09387
-2.34	0.09412	0.09437	0.09463	0.09488	0.09514	0.09539	0.09565	0.09590	0.09616	0.09642
-2.33	0.09668	0.09694	0.09720	0.09746	0.09772	0.09798	0.09824	0.09850	0.09877	0.09903
-2.32	0.09930	0.09956	0.09983	0.10009	0.10036	0.10063	0.10090	0.10116	0.10143	0.10170
-2.31	0.10198	0.10225	0.10252	0.10279	0.10306	0.10334	0.10361	0.10389	0.10416	0.10444
-2.30	0.10472	0.10500	0.10527	0.10555	0.10583	0.10611	0.10639	0.10668	0.10696	0.10724
-2.29	0.10752	0.10781	0.10809	0.10838	0.10867	0.10895	0.10924	0.10953	0.10982	0.11011
-2.28	0.11040	0.11069	0.11098	0.11127	0.11156	0.11186	0.11215	0.11245	0.11274	0.11304
-2.27	0.11334	0.11363	0.11393	0.11423	0.11453	0.11483	0.11513	0.11543	0.11573	0.11604
-2.26	0.11634	0.11665	0.11695	0.11726	0.11756	0.11787	0.11818	0.11849	0.11880	0.11911
-2.25	0.11942	0.11973	0.12004	0.12035	0.12067	0.12098	0.12130	0.12161	0.12193	0.12224
-2.24	0.12256	0.12288	0.12320	0.12352	0.12384	0.12416	0.12448	0.12481	0.12513	0.12545

continued

continued

$\frac{x-\mu}{\sigma}$	0.009	0.008	0.007	0.006	0.005	0.004	0.003	0.002	0.001	0.000
−2.23	0.12578	0.12611	0.12643	0.12676	0.12709	0.12742	0.12774	0.12807	0.12841	0.12874
−2.22	0.12907	0.12940	0.12974	0.13007	0.13041	0.13074	0.13108	0.13142	0.13175	0.13209
−2.21	0.13243	0.13277	0.13312	0.13346	0.13380	0.13414	0.13449	0.13483	0.13518	0.13553
−2.20	0.13587	0.13622	0.13657	0.13692	0.13727	0.13762	0.13797	0.13833	0.13868	0.13903
−2.19	0.13939	0.13975	0.14010	0.14046	0.14082	0.14118	0.14154	0.14190	0.14226	0.14262
−2.18	0.14298	0.14335	0.14371	0.14408	0.14444	0.14481	0.14518	0.14555	0.14592	0.14629
−2.17	0.14666	0.14703	0.14740	0.14778	0.14815	0.14853	0.14890	0.14928	0.14966	0.15003
−2.16	0.15041	0.15079	0.15117	0.15156	0.15194	0.15232	0.15271	0.15309	0.15348	0.15386
−2.15	0.15425	0.15464	0.15503	0.15542	0.15581	0.15620	0.15659	0.15699	0.15738	0.15778
−2.14	0.15817	0.15857	0.15897	0.15936	0.15976	0.16016	0.16057	0.16097	0.16137	0.16177
−2.13	0.16218	0.16258	0.16299	0.16340	0.16381	0.16421	0.16462	0.16503	0.16545	0.16586
−2.12	0.16627	0.16669	0.16710	0.16752	0.16793	0.16835	0.16877	0.16919	0.16961	0.17003
−2.11	0.17045	0.17088	0.17130	0.17172	0.17215	0.17258	0.17300	0.17343	0.17386	0.17429
−2.10	0.17472	0.17515	0.17559	0.17602	0.17646	0.17689	0.17733	0.17777	0.17820	0.17864
−2.09	0.17908	0.17953	0.17997	0.18041	0.18085	0.18130	0.18175	0.18219	0.18264	0.18309
−2.08	0.18354	0.18399	0.18444	0.18489	0.18535	0.18580	0.18626	0.18671	0.18717	0.18763
−2.07	0.18809	0.18855	0.18901	0.18947	0.18993	0.19040	0.19086	0.19133	0.19179	0.19226
−2.06	0.19273	0.19320	0.19367	0.19414	0.19462	0.19509	0.19556	0.19604	0.19652	0.19699
−2.05	0.19747	0.19795	0.19843	0.19891	0.19940	0.19988	0.20036	0.20085	0.20133	0.20182
−2.04	0.20231	0.20280	0.20329	0.20378	0.20427	0.20477	0.20526	0.20576	0.20625	0.20675
−2.03	0.20725	0.20775	0.20825	0.20875	0.20925	0.20976	0.21026	0.21077	0.21127	0.21178
−2.02	0.21229	0.21280	0.21331	0.21382	0.21434	0.21485	0.21537	0.21588	0.21640	0.21692
−2.01	0.21744	0.21796	0.21848	0.21900	0.21952	0.22005	0.22057	0.22110	0.22163	0.22216
−2.00	0.22269	0.22322	0.22375	0.22428	0.22482	0.22535	0.22589	0.22642	0.22696	0.22750

Table 1E   Areas under the normal curve from $Z = -2.000$ to -1.500.

The proportion of total area (α) under the curve that is under the portion of the curve from $-\infty$ to $\dfrac{x - \mu}{\sigma}$ (x represents any desired value of the variable x). Note: entries must be multiplied by 10^{-1}.

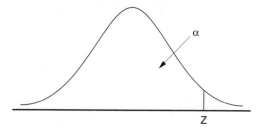

$\dfrac{x-\mu}{\sigma}$	0.009	0.008	0.007	0.006	0.005	0.004	0.003	0.002	0.001	0.000
-2.00	0.22269	0.22322	0.22375	0.22428	0.22482	0.22535	0.22589	0.22642	0.22696	0.22750
-1.99	0.22804	0.22858	0.22913	0.22967	0.23021	0.23076	0.23131	0.23186	0.23240	0.23295
-1.98	0.23351	0.23406	0.23461	0.23517	0.23572	0.23628	0.23684	0.23740	0.23796	0.23852
-1.97	0.23908	0.23964	0.24021	0.24077	0.24134	0.24191	0.24248	0.24305	0.24362	0.24419
-1.96	0.24477	0.24534	0.24592	0.24649	0.24707	0.24765	0.24823	0.24881	0.24940	0.24998
-1.95	0.25056	0.25115	0.25174	0.25233	0.25292	0.25351	0.25410	0.25469	0.25529	0.25588
-1.94	0.25648	0.25707	0.25767	0.25827	0.25887	0.25948	0.26008	0.26069	0.26129	0.26190
-1.93	0.26251	0.26312	0.26373	0.26434	0.26495	0.26557	0.26618	0.26680	0.26742	0.26803
-1.92	0.26865	0.26928	0.26990	0.27052	0.27115	0.27177	0.27240	0.27303	0.27366	0.27429
-1.91	0.27492	0.27556	0.27619	0.27683	0.27746	0.27810	0.27874	0.27938	0.28002	0.28067
-1.90	0.28131	0.28196	0.28260	0.28325	0.28390	0.28455	0.28520	0.28586	0.28651	0.28717
-1.89	0.28782	0.28848	0.28914	0.28980	0.29046	0.29113	0.29179	0.29245	0.29312	0.29379
-1.88	0.29446	0.29513	0.29580	0.29647	0.29715	0.29782	0.29850	0.29918	0.29986	0.30054
-1.87	0.30122	0.30191	0.30259	0.30328	0.30396	0.30465	0.30534	0.30603	0.30673	0.30742
-1.86	0.30811	0.30881	0.30951	0.31021	0.31091	0.31161	0.31231	0.31302	0.31372	0.31443
-1.85	0.31514	0.31585	0.31656	0.31727	0.31798	0.31870	0.31941	0.32013	0.32085	0.32157
-1.84	0.32229	0.32301	0.32374	0.32446	0.32519	0.32592	0.32665	0.32738	0.32811	0.32884
-1.83	0.32958	0.33031	0.33105	0.33179	0.33253	0.33327	0.33401	0.33476	0.33550	0.33625
-1.82	0.33700	0.33775	0.33850	0.33925	0.34001	0.34076	0.34152	0.34227	0.34303	0.34380
-1.81	0.34456	0.34532	0.34609	0.34685	0.34762	0.34839	0.34916	0.34993	0.35070	0.35148
-1.80	0.35226	0.35303	0.35381	0.35459	0.35537	0.35616	0.35694	0.35773	0.35851	0.35930
-1.79	0.36009	0.36089	0.36168	0.36247	0.36327	0.36407	0.36486	0.36566	0.36647	0.36727
-1.78	0.36807	0.36888	0.36969	0.37050	0.37131	0.37212	0.37293	0.37375	0.37456	0.37538
-1.77	0.37620	0.37702	0.37784	0.37866	0.37949	0.38032	0.38114	0.38197	0.38280	0.38364
-1.76	0.38447	0.38530	0.38614	0.38698	0.38782	0.38866	0.38950	0.39035	0.39119	0.39204
-1.75	0.39289	0.39374	0.39459	0.39544	0.39630	0.39715	0.39801	0.39887	0.39973	0.40059
-1.74	0.40146	0.40232	0.40319	0.40405	0.40492	0.40580	0.40667	0.40754	0.40842	0.40930

continued

continued

$\frac{x-\mu}{\sigma}$	0.009	0.008	0.007	0.006	0.005	0.004	0.003	0.002	0.001	0.000
−1.73	0.41017	0.41105	0.41194	0.41282	0.41370	0.41459	0.41548	0.41637	0.41726	0.41815
−1.72	0.41905	0.41994	0.42084	0.42174	0.42264	0.42354	0.42444	0.42535	0.42625	0.42716
−1.71	0.42807	0.42898	0.42990	0.43081	0.43173	0.43264	0.43356	0.43448	0.43541	0.43633
−1.70	0.43725	0.43818	0.43911	0.44004	0.44097	0.44191	0.44284	0.44378	0.44471	0.44565
−1.69	0.44660	0.44754	0.44848	0.44943	0.45038	0.45133	0.45228	0.45323	0.45418	0.45514
−1.68	0.45610	0.45706	0.45802	0.45898	0.45994	0.46091	0.46188	0.46284	0.46381	0.46479
−1.67	0.46576	0.46674	0.46771	0.46869	0.46967	0.47065	0.47164	0.47262	0.47361	0.47460
−1.66	0.47559	0.47658	0.47757	0.47857	0.47956	0.48056	0.48156	0.48256	0.48357	0.48457
−1.65	0.48558	0.48659	0.48760	0.48861	0.48962	0.49064	0.49165	0.49267	0.49369	0.49471
−1.64	0.49574	0.49676	0.49779	0.49882	0.49985	0.50088	0.50191	0.50295	0.50399	0.50503
−1.63	0.50607	0.50711	0.50815	0.50920	0.51025	0.51129	0.51234	0.51340	0.51445	0.51551
−1.62	0.51657	0.51762	0.51869	0.51975	0.52081	0.52188	0.52295	0.52402	0.52509	0.52616
−1.61	0.52724	0.52831	0.52939	0.53047	0.53155	0.53264	0.53372	0.53481	0.53590	0.53699
−1.60	0.53808	0.53918	0.54027	0.54137	0.54247	0.54357	0.54467	0.54578	0.54688	0.54799
−1.59	0.54910	0.55021	0.55133	0.55244	0.55356	0.55468	0.55580	0.55692	0.55805	0.55917
−1.58	0.56030	0.56143	0.56256	0.56370	0.56483	0.56597	0.56711	0.56825	0.56939	0.57053
−1.57	0.57168	0.57283	0.57398	0.57513	0.57628	0.57744	0.57859	0.57975	0.58091	0.58208
−1.56	0.58324	0.58441	0.58557	0.58674	0.58791	0.58909	0.59026	0.59144	0.59262	0.59380
−1.55	0.59498	0.59617	0.59735	0.59854	0.59973	0.60092	0.60212	0.60331	0.60451	0.60571
−1.54	0.60691	0.60811	0.60932	0.61052	0.61173	0.61294	0.61415	0.61537	0.61658	0.61780
−1.53	0.61902	0.62024	0.62147	0.62269	0.62392	0.62515	0.62638	0.62761	0.62885	0.63008
−1.52	0.63132	0.63256	0.63381	0.63505	0.63630	0.63754	0.63879	0.64005	0.64130	0.64255
−1.51	0.64381	0.64507	0.64633	0.64760	0.64886	0.65013	0.65140	0.65267	0.65394	0.65522
−1.50	0.65649	0.65777	0.65905	0.66034	0.66162	0.66291	0.66420	0.66549	0.66678	0.66807

Table 1F Areas under the normal curve from $Z = -1.500$ to -1.000.

The proportion of total area (α) under the curve that is under the portion of the curve from $-\infty$ to $\dfrac{x-\mu}{\sigma}$ (x represents any desired value of the variable x).

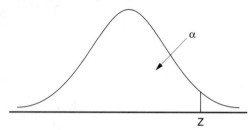

$\dfrac{x-\mu}{\sigma}$	0.009	0.008	0.007	0.006	0.005	0.004	0.003	0.002	0.001	0.000
−1.50	0.06565	0.06578	0.06591	0.06603	0.06616	0.06629	0.06642	0.06655	0.06668	0.06681
−1.49	0.06694	0.06707	0.06720	0.06733	0.06746	0.06759	0.06772	0.06785	0.06798	0.06811
−1.48	0.06824	0.06838	0.06851	0.06864	0.06877	0.06890	0.06904	0.06917	0.06930	0.06944
−1.47	0.06957	0.06970	0.06984	0.06997	0.07011	0.07024	0.07038	0.07051	0.07065	0.07078
−1.46	0.07092	0.07105	0.07119	0.07132	0.07146	0.07160	0.07173	0.07187	0.07201	0.07215
−1.45	0.07228	0.07242	0.07256	0.07270	0.07283	0.07297	0.07311	0.07325	0.07339	0.07353
−1.44	0.07367	0.07381	0.07395	0.07409	0.07423	0.07437	0.07451	0.07465	0.07479	0.07493
−1.43	0.07508	0.07522	0.07536	0.07550	0.07564	0.07579	0.07593	0.07607	0.07622	0.07636
−1.42	0.07650	0.07665	0.07679	0.07693	0.07708	0.07722	0.07737	0.07751	0.07766	0.07780
−1.41	0.07795	0.07810	0.07824	0.07839	0.07853	0.07868	0.07883	0.07897	0.07912	0.07927
−1.40	0.07942	0.07957	0.07971	0.07986	0.08001	0.08016	0.08031	0.08046	0.08061	0.08076
−1.39	0.08091	0.08106	0.08121	0.08136	0.08151	0.08166	0.08181	0.08196	0.08211	0.08226
−1.38	0.08242	0.08257	0.08272	0.08287	0.08303	0.08318	0.08333	0.08349	0.08364	0.08379
−1.37	0.08395	0.08410	0.08426	0.08441	0.08457	0.08472	0.08488	0.08503	0.08519	0.08534
−1.36	0.08550	0.08566	0.08581	0.08597	0.08613	0.08628	0.08644	0.08660	0.08676	0.08691
−1.35	0.08707	0.08723	0.08739	0.08755	0.08771	0.08787	0.08803	0.08819	0.08835	0.08851
−1.34	0.08867	0.08883	0.08899	0.08915	0.08931	0.08947	0.08964	0.08980	0.08996	0.09012
−1.33	0.09029	0.09045	0.09061	0.09077	0.09094	0.09110	0.09127	0.09143	0.09159	0.09176
−1.32	0.09192	0.09209	0.09225	0.09242	0.09259	0.09275	0.09292	0.09308	0.09325	0.09342
−1.31	0.09358	0.09375	0.09392	0.09409	0.09425	0.09442	0.09459	0.09476	0.09493	0.09510
−1.30	0.09527	0.09544	0.09561	0.09578	0.09595	0.09612	0.09629	0.09646	0.09663	0.09680
−1.29	0.09697	0.09714	0.09732	0.09749	0.09766	0.09783	0.09801	0.09818	0.09835	0.09853
−1.28	0.09870	0.09887	0.09905	0.09922	0.09940	0.09957	0.09975	0.09992	0.10010	0.10027
−1.27	0.10045	0.10062	0.10080	0.10098	0.10115	0.10133	0.10151	0.10169	0.10186	0.10204
−1.26	0.10222	0.10240	0.10258	0.10276	0.10294	0.10312	0.10329	0.10347	0.10365	0.10383
−1.25	0.10402	0.10420	0.10438	0.10456	0.10474	0.10492	0.10510	0.10528	0.10547	0.10565
−1.24	0.10583	0.10602	0.10620	0.10638	0.10657	0.10675	0.10693	0.10712	0.10730	0.10749

continued

continued

$\dfrac{x-\mu}{\sigma}$	0.009	0.008	0.007	0.006	0.005	0.004	0.003	0.002	0.001	0.000
−1.23	0.10767	0.10786	0.10804	0.10823	0.10842	0.10860	0.10879	0.10897	0.10916	0.10935
−1.22	0.10954	0.10972	0.10991	0.11010	0.11029	0.11048	0.11066	0.11085	0.11104	0.11123
−1.21	0.11142	0.11161	0.11180	0.11199	0.11218	0.11237	0.11256	0.11276	0.11295	0.11314
−1.20	0.11333	0.11352	0.11372	0.11391	0.11410	0.11429	0.11449	0.11468	0.11488	0.11507
−1.19	0.11526	0.11546	0.11565	0.11585	0.11604	0.11624	0.11643	0.11663	0.11683	0.11702
−1.18	0.11722	0.11742	0.11761	0.11781	0.11801	0.11821	0.11840	0.11860	0.11880	0.11900
−1.17	0.11920	0.11940	0.11960	0.11980	0.12000	0.12020	0.12040	0.12060	0.12080	0.12100
−1.16	0.12120	0.12140	0.12161	0.12181	0.12201	0.12221	0.12241	0.12262	0.12282	0.12302
−1.15	0.12323	0.12343	0.12364	0.12384	0.12405	0.12425	0.12446	0.12466	0.12487	0.12507
−1.14	0.12528	0.12548	0.12569	0.12590	0.12610	0.12631	0.12652	0.12673	0.12693	0.12714
−1.13	0.12735	0.12756	0.12777	0.12798	0.12819	0.12840	0.12861	0.12882	0.12903	0.12924
−1.12	0.12945	0.12966	0.12987	0.13008	0.13029	0.13051	0.13072	0.13093	0.13114	0.13136
−1.11	0.13157	0.13178	0.13200	0.13221	0.13243	0.13264	0.13285	0.13307	0.13328	0.13350
−1.10	0.13372	0.13393	0.13415	0.13436	0.13458	0.13480	0.13501	0.13523	0.13545	0.13567
−1.09	0.13588	0.13610	0.13632	0.13654	0.13676	0.13698	0.13720	0.13742	0.13764	0.13786
−1.08	0.13808	0.13830	0.13852	0.13874	0.13896	0.13918	0.13940	0.13963	0.13985	0.14007
−1.07	0.14029	0.14052	0.14074	0.14096	0.14119	0.14141	0.14164	0.14186	0.14208	0.14231
−1.06	0.14253	0.14276	0.14299	0.14321	0.14344	0.14366	0.14389	0.14412	0.14434	0.14457
−1.05	0.14480	0.14503	0.14526	0.14548	0.14571	0.14594	0.14617	0.14640	0.14663	0.14686
−1.04	0.14709	0.14732	0.14755	0.14778	0.14801	0.14824	0.14847	0.14871	0.14894	0.14917
−1.03	0.14940	0.14964	0.14987	0.15010	0.15033	0.15057	0.15080	0.15104	0.15127	0.15151
−1.02	0.15174	0.15197	0.15221	0.15245	0.15268	0.15292	0.15315	0.15339	0.15363	0.15386
−1.01	0.15410	0.15434	0.15458	0.15481	0.15505	0.15529	0.15553	0.15577	0.15601	0.15625
−1.00	0.15649	0.15673	0.15697	0.15721	0.15745	0.15769	0.15793	0.15817	0.15841	0.15866

Table 1G Areas under the normal curve from $Z = -1.000$ to -0.500.

The proportion of total area (α) under the curve that is under the portion of the curve from $-\infty$ to $\dfrac{x-\mu}{\sigma}$ (x represents any desired value of the variable x).

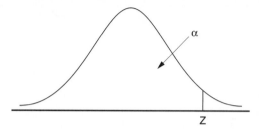

$\dfrac{x-\mu}{\sigma}$	0.009	0.008	0.007	0.006	0.005	0.004	0.003	0.002	0.001	0.000
−1.00	0.15649	0.15673	0.15697	0.15721	0.15745	0.15769	0.15793	0.15817	0.15841	0.15866
−0.99	0.15890	0.15914	0.15938	0.15963	0.15987	0.16011	0.16035	0.16060	0.16084	0.16109
−0.98	0.16133	0.16158	0.16182	0.16207	0.16231	0.16256	0.16280	0.16305	0.16330	0.16354
−0.97	0.16379	0.16404	0.16428	0.16453	0.16478	0.16503	0.16528	0.16553	0.16577	0.16602
−0.96	0.16627	0.16652	0.16677	0.16702	0.16727	0.16752	0.16777	0.16802	0.16828	0.16853
−0.95	0.16878	0.16903	0.16928	0.16954	0.16979	0.17004	0.17030	0.17055	0.17080	0.17106
−0.94	0.17131	0.17156	0.17182	0.17207	0.17233	0.17258	0.17284	0.17310	0.17335	0.17361
−0.93	0.17387	0.17412	0.17438	0.17464	0.17489	0.17515	0.17541	0.17567	0.17593	0.17619
−0.92	0.17644	0.17670	0.17696	0.17722	0.17748	0.17774	0.17800	0.17826	0.17853	0.17879
−0.91	0.17905	0.17931	0.17957	0.17983	0.18010	0.18036	0.18062	0.18088	0.18115	0.18141
−0.90	0.18168	0.18194	0.18220	0.18247	0.18273	0.18300	0.18326	0.18353	0.18379	0.18406
−0.89	0.18433	0.18459	0.18486	0.18513	0.18539	0.18566	0.18593	0.18620	0.18646	0.18673
−0.88	0.18700	0.18727	0.18754	0.18781	0.18808	0.18835	0.18862	0.18889	0.18916	0.18943
−0.87	0.18970	0.18997	0.19024	0.19052	0.19079	0.19106	0.19133	0.19160	0.19188	0.19215
−0.86	0.19242	0.19270	0.19297	0.19325	0.19352	0.19379	0.19407	0.19434	0.19462	0.19489
−0.85	0.19517	0.19545	0.19572	0.19600	0.19628	0.19655	0.19683	0.19711	0.19738	0.19766
−0.84	0.19794	0.19822	0.19850	0.19878	0.19906	0.19933	0.19961	0.19989	0.20017	0.20045
−0.83	0.20073	0.20102	0.20130	0.20158	0.20186	0.20214	0.20242	0.20270	0.20299	0.20327
−0.82	0.20355	0.20384	0.20412	0.20440	0.20469	0.20497	0.20525	0.20554	0.20582	0.20611
−0.81	0.20639	0.20668	0.20696	0.20725	0.20754	0.20782	0.20811	0.20840	0.20868	0.20897
−0.80	0.20926	0.20955	0.20983	0.21012	0.21041	0.21070	0.21099	0.21128	0.21157	0.21186
−0.79	0.21215	0.21244	0.21273	0.21302	0.21331	0.21360	0.21389	0.21418	0.21447	0.21476
−0.78	0.21506	0.21535	0.21564	0.21593	0.21623	0.21652	0.21681	0.21711	0.21740	0.21770
−0.77	0.21799	0.21828	0.21858	0.21887	0.21917	0.21947	0.21976	0.22006	0.22035	0.22065
−0.76	0.22095	0.22124	0.22154	0.22184	0.22214	0.22243	0.22273	0.22303	0.22333	0.22363
−0.75	0.22393	0.22423	0.22452	0.22482	0.22512	0.22542	0.22572	0.22603	0.22633	0.22663
−0.74	0.22693	0.22723	0.22753	0.22783	0.22814	0.22844	0.22874	0.22904	0.22935	0.22965

continued

continued

$\frac{x-\mu}{\sigma}$	0.009	0.008	0.007	0.006	0.005	0.004	0.003	0.002	0.001	0.000
−0.73	0.22995	0.23026	0.23056	0.23087	0.23117	0.23147	0.23178	0.23208	0.23239	0.23270
−0.72	0.23300	0.23331	0.23361	0.23392	0.23423	0.23453	0.23484	0.23515	0.23545	0.23576
−0.71	0.23607	0.23638	0.23669	0.23700	0.23730	0.23761	0.23792	0.23823	0.23854	0.23885
−0.70	0.23916	0.23947	0.23978	0.24009	0.24041	0.24072	0.24103	0.24134	0.24165	0.24196
−0.69	0.24228	0.24259	0.24290	0.24321	0.24353	0.24384	0.24415	0.24447	0.24478	0.24510
−0.68	0.24541	0.24573	0.24604	0.24636	0.24667	0.24699	0.24730	0.24762	0.24794	0.24825
−0.67	0.24857	0.24889	0.24920	0.24952	0.24984	0.25016	0.25047	0.25079	0.25111	0.25143
−0.66	0.25175	0.25207	0.25239	0.25271	0.25303	0.25335	0.25367	0.25399	0.25431	0.25463
−0.65	0.25495	0.25527	0.25559	0.25591	0.25623	0.25656	0.25688	0.25720	0.25752	0.25785
−0.64	0.25817	0.25849	0.25882	0.25914	0.25946	0.25979	0.26011	0.26044	0.26076	0.26109
−0.63	0.26141	0.26174	0.26206	0.26239	0.26271	0.26304	0.26337	0.26369	0.26402	0.26435
−0.62	0.26467	0.26500	0.26533	0.26566	0.26599	0.26631	0.26664	0.26697	0.26730	0.26763
−0.61	0.26796	0.26829	0.26862	0.26895	0.26928	0.26961	0.26994	0.27027	0.27060	0.27093
−0.60	0.27126	0.27159	0.27193	0.27226	0.27259	0.27292	0.27325	0.27359	0.27392	0.27425
−0.59	0.27459	0.27492	0.27525	0.27559	0.27592	0.27626	0.27659	0.27693	0.27726	0.27760
−0.58	0.27793	0.27827	0.27860	0.27894	0.27927	0.27961	0.27995	0.28028	0.28062	0.28096
−0.57	0.28129	0.28163	0.28197	0.28231	0.28265	0.28298	0.28332	0.28366	0.28400	0.28434
−0.56	0.28468	0.28502	0.28536	0.28570	0.28604	0.28638	0.28672	0.28706	0.28740	0.28774
−0.55	0.28808	0.28842	0.28876	0.28911	0.28945	0.28979	0.29013	0.29047	0.29082	0.29116
−0.54	0.29150	0.29185	0.29219	0.29253	0.29288	0.29322	0.29356	0.29391	0.29425	0.29460
−0.53	0.29494	0.29529	0.29563	0.29598	0.29632	0.29667	0.29702	0.29736	0.29771	0.29806
−0.52	0.29840	0.29875	0.29910	0.29944	0.29979	0.30014	0.30049	0.30084	0.30118	0.30153
−0.51	0.30188	0.30223	0.30258	0.30293	0.30328	0.30363	0.30398	0.30433	0.30468	0.30503
−0.50	0.30538	0.30573	0.30608	0.30643	0.30678	0.30713	0.30748	0.30783	0.30819	0.30854

Table 1H Areas under the normal curve from $Z = -0.500$ to 0.000.

The proportion of total area (α) under the curve that is under the portion of the curve from $-\infty$ to $\frac{x-\mu}{\sigma}$ (x represents any desired value of the variable x).

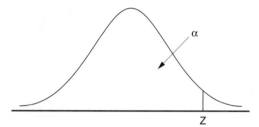

$\frac{x-\mu}{\sigma}$	0.009	0.008	0.007	0.006	0.005	0.004	0.003	0.002	0.001	0.000
−0.50	0.30538	0.30573	0.30608	0.30643	0.30678	0.30713	0.30748	0.30783	0.30819	0.30854
−0.49	0.30889	0.30924	0.30959	0.30995	0.31030	0.31065	0.31101	0.31136	0.31171	0.31207
−0.48	0.31242	0.31277	0.31313	0.31348	0.31384	0.31419	0.31455	0.31490	0.31526	0.31561
−0.47	0.31597	0.31633	0.31668	0.31704	0.31739	0.31775	0.31811	0.31846	0.31882	0.31918
−0.46	0.31953	0.31989	0.32025	0.32061	0.32097	0.32132	0.32168	0.32204	0.32240	0.32276
−0.45	0.32312	0.32348	0.32384	0.32419	0.32455	0.32491	0.32527	0.32563	0.32599	0.32636
−0.44	0.32672	0.32708	0.32744	0.32780	0.32816	0.32852	0.32888	0.32924	0.32961	0.32997
−0.43	0.33033	0.33069	0.33106	0.33142	0.33178	0.33214	0.33251	0.33287	0.33323	0.33360
−0.42	0.33396	0.33433	0.33469	0.33505	0.33542	0.33578	0.33615	0.33651	0.33688	0.33724
−0.41	0.33761	0.33797	0.33834	0.33871	0.33907	0.33944	0.33980	0.34017	0.34054	0.34090
−0.40	0.34127	0.34164	0.34200	0.34237	0.34274	0.34311	0.34347	0.34384	0.34421	0.34458
−0.39	0.34495	0.34532	0.34568	0.34605	0.34642	0.34679	0.34716	0.34753	0.34790	0.34827
−0.38	0.34864	0.34901	0.34938	0.34975	0.35012	0.35049	0.35086	0.35123	0.35160	0.35197
−0.37	0.35234	0.35272	0.35309	0.35346	0.35383	0.35420	0.35457	0.35495	0.35532	0.35569
−0.36	0.35606	0.35644	0.35681	0.35718	0.35756	0.35793	0.35830	0.35868	0.35905	0.35942
−0.35	0.35980	0.36017	0.36055	0.36092	0.36129	0.36167	0.36204	0.36242	0.36279	0.36317
−0.34	0.36354	0.36392	0.36430	0.36467	0.36505	0.36542	0.36580	0.36618	0.36655	0.36693
−0.33	0.36730	0.36768	0.36806	0.36844	0.36881	0.36919	0.36957	0.36994	0.37032	0.37070
−0.32	0.37108	0.37146	0.37183	0.37221	0.37259	0.37297	0.37335	0.37373	0.37411	0.37448
−0.31	0.37486	0.37524	0.37562	0.37600	0.37638	0.37676	0.37714	0.37752	0.37790	0.37828
−0.30	0.37866	0.37904	0.37942	0.37980	0.38018	0.38056	0.38094	0.38133	0.38171	0.38209
−0.29	0.38247	0.38285	0.38323	0.38362	0.38400	0.38438	0.38476	0.38514	0.38553	0.38591
−0.28	0.38629	0.38667	0.38706	0.38744	0.38782	0.38821	0.38859	0.38897	0.38936	0.38974
−0.27	0.39012	0.39051	0.39089	0.39127	0.39166	0.39204	0.39243	0.39281	0.39320	0.39358
−0.26	0.39396	0.39435	0.39473	0.39512	0.39550	0.39589	0.39628	0.39666	0.39705	0.39743
−0.25	0.39782	0.39820	0.39859	0.39898	0.39936	0.39975	0.40013	0.40052	0.40091	0.40129
−0.24	0.40168	0.40207	0.40245	0.40284	0.40323	0.40362	0.40400	0.40439	0.40478	0.40517

continued

continued

$\frac{x-\mu}{\sigma}$	0.009	0.008	0.007	0.006	0.005	0.004	0.003	0.002	0.001	0.000
−0.23	0.40555	0.40594	0.40633	0.40672	0.40710	0.40749	0.40788	0.40827	0.40866	0.40905
−0.22	0.40943	0.40982	0.41021	0.41060	0.41099	0.41138	0.41177	0.41216	0.41255	0.41294
−0.21	0.41333	0.41371	0.41410	0.41449	0.41488	0.41527	0.41566	0.41605	0.41644	0.41683
−0.20	0.41722	0.41761	0.41800	0.41840	0.41879	0.41918	0.41957	0.41996	0.42035	0.42074
−0.19	0.42113	0.42152	0.42191	0.42231	0.42270	0.42309	0.42348	0.42387	0.42426	0.42465
−0.18	0.42505	0.42544	0.42583	0.42622	0.42661	0.42701	0.42740	0.42779	0.42818	0.42858
−0.17	0.42897	0.42936	0.42975	0.43015	0.43054	0.43093	0.43133	0.43172	0.43211	0.43251
−0.16	0.43290	0.43329	0.43369	0.43408	0.43447	0.43487	0.43526	0.43565	0.43605	0.43644
−0.15	0.43683	0.43723	0.43762	0.43802	0.43841	0.43880	0.43920	0.43959	0.43999	0.44038
−0.14	0.44078	0.44117	0.44157	0.44196	0.44236	0.44275	0.44315	0.44354	0.44393	0.44433
−0.13	0.44473	0.44512	0.44552	0.44591	0.44631	0.44670	0.44710	0.44749	0.44789	0.44828
−0.12	0.44868	0.44907	0.44947	0.44987	0.45026	0.45066	0.45105	0.45145	0.45185	0.45224
−0.11	0.45264	0.45303	0.45343	0.45383	0.45422	0.45462	0.45502	0.45541	0.45581	0.45620
−0.10	0.45660	0.45700	0.45739	0.45779	0.45819	0.45858	0.45898	0.45938	0.45978	0.46017
−0.09	0.46057	0.46097	0.46136	0.46176	0.46216	0.46255	0.46295	0.46335	0.46375	0.46414
−0.08	0.46454	0.46494	0.46534	0.46573	0.46613	0.46653	0.46693	0.46732	0.46772	0.46812
−0.07	0.46852	0.46891	0.46931	0.46971	0.47011	0.47051	0.47090	0.47130	0.47170	0.47210
−0.06	0.47249	0.47289	0.47329	0.47369	0.47409	0.47449	0.47488	0.47528	0.47568	0.47608
−0.05	0.47648	0.47687	0.47727	0.47767	0.47807	0.47847	0.47887	0.47926	0.47966	0.48006
−0.04	0.48046	0.48086	0.48126	0.48166	0.48205	0.48245	0.48285	0.48325	0.48365	0.48405
−0.03	0.48445	0.48484	0.48524	0.48564	0.48604	0.48644	0.48684	0.48724	0.48763	0.48803
−0.02	0.48843	0.48883	0.48923	0.48963	0.49003	0.49043	0.49083	0.49122	0.49162	0.49202
−0.01	0.49242	0.49282	0.49322	0.49362	0.49402	0.49441	0.49481	0.49521	0.49561	0.49601
−0.00	0.49641	0.49681	0.49721	0.49761	0.49801	0.49840	0.49880	0.49920	0.49960	0.50000

Table 1J   Areas under the normal curve from Z = 0.000 to 0.500.

The proportion of total area (α) under the curve that is under the portion of the curve from $-\infty$ to $\frac{x-\mu}{\sigma}$ (x represents any desired value of the variable x).

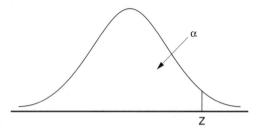

$\frac{x-\mu}{\sigma}$	0.000	0.001	0.002	0.003	0.004	0.005	0.006	0.007	0.008	0.009
0.00	0.50000	0.50040	0.50080	0.50120	0.50160	0.50199	0.50239	0.50279	0.50319	0.50359
0.01	0.50399	0.50439	0.50479	0.50519	0.50559	0.50598	0.50638	0.50678	0.50718	0.50758
0.02	0.50798	0.50838	0.50878	0.50917	0.50957	0.50997	0.51037	0.51077	0.51117	0.51157
0.03	0.51197	0.51237	0.51276	0.51316	0.51356	0.51396	0.51436	0.51476	0.51516	0.51555
0.04	0.51595	0.51635	0.51675	0.51715	0.51755	0.51795	0.51834	0.51874	0.51914	0.51954
0.05	0.51994	0.52034	0.52074	0.52113	0.52153	0.52193	0.52233	0.52273	0.52313	0.52352
0.06	0.52392	0.52432	0.52472	0.52512	0.52551	0.52591	0.52631	0.52671	0.52711	0.52751
0.07	0.52790	0.52830	0.52870	0.52910	0.52949	0.52989	0.53029	0.53069	0.53109	0.53148
0.08	0.53188	0.53228	0.53268	0.53307	0.53347	0.53387	0.53427	0.53466	0.53506	0.53546
0.09	0.53586	0.53625	0.53665	0.53705	0.53745	0.53784	0.53824	0.53864	0.53903	0.53943
0.10	0.53983	0.54022	0.54062	0.54102	0.54142	0.54181	0.54221	0.54261	0.54300	0.54340
0.11	0.54380	0.54419	0.54459	0.54498	0.54538	0.54578	0.54617	0.54657	0.54697	0.54736
0.12	0.54776	0.54815	0.54855	0.54895	0.54934	0.54974	0.55013	0.55053	0.55093	0.55132
0.13	0.55172	0.55211	0.55251	0.55290	0.55330	0.55369	0.55409	0.55448	0.55488	0.55527
0.14	0.55567	0.55607	0.55646	0.55685	0.55725	0.55764	0.55804	0.55843	0.55883	0.55922
0.15	0.55962	0.56001	0.56041	0.56080	0.56120	0.56159	0.56198	0.56238	0.56277	0.56317
0.16	0.56356	0.56395	0.56435	0.56474	0.56513	0.56553	0.56592	0.56631	0.56671	0.56710
0.17	0.56749	0.56789	0.56828	0.56867	0.56907	0.56946	0.56985	0.57025	0.57064	0.57103
0.18	0.57142	0.57182	0.57221	0.57260	0.57299	0.57339	0.57378	0.57417	0.57456	0.57495
0.19	0.57535	0.57574	0.57613	0.57652	0.57691	0.57730	0.57769	0.57809	0.57848	0.57887
0.20	0.57926	0.57965	0.58004	0.58043	0.58082	0.58121	0.58160	0.58200	0.58239	0.58278
0.21	0.58317	0.58356	0.58395	0.58434	0.58473	0.58512	0.58551	0.58590	0.58629	0.58667
0.22	0.58706	0.58745	0.58784	0.58823	0.58862	0.58901	0.58940	0.58979	0.59018	0.59057
0.23	0.59095	0.59134	0.59173	0.59212	0.59251	0.59290	0.59328	0.59367	0.59406	0.59445
0.24	0.59483	0.59522	0.59561	0.59600	0.59638	0.59677	0.59716	0.59755	0.59793	0.59832
0.25	0.59871	0.59909	0.59948	0.59987	0.60025	0.60064	0.60102	0.60141	0.60180	0.60218
0.26	0.60257	0.60295	0.60334	0.60372	0.60411	0.60450	0.60488	0.60527	0.60565	0.60604

continued

continued

$\dfrac{x-\mu}{\sigma}$	0.000	0.001	0.002	0.003	0.004	0.005	0.006	0.007	0.008	0.009
0.27	0.60642	0.60680	0.60719	0.60757	0.60796	0.60834	0.60873	0.60911	0.60949	0.60988
0.28	0.61026	0.61064	0.61103	0.61141	0.61179	0.61218	0.61256	0.61294	0.61333	0.61371
0.29	0.61409	0.61447	0.61486	0.61524	0.61562	0.61600	0.61638	0.61677	0.61715	0.61753
0.30	0.61791	0.61829	0.61867	0.61906	0.61944	0.61982	0.62020	0.62058	0.62096	0.62134
0.31	0.62172	0.62210	0.62248	0.62286	0.62324	0.62362	0.62400	0.62438	0.62476	0.62514
0.32	0.62552	0.62589	0.62627	0.62665	0.62703	0.62741	0.62779	0.62817	0.62854	0.62892
0.33	0.62930	0.62968	0.63006	0.63043	0.63081	0.63119	0.63156	0.63194	0.63232	0.63270
0.34	0.63307	0.63345	0.63382	0.63420	0.63458	0.63495	0.63533	0.63570	0.63608	0.63646
0.35	0.63683	0.63721	0.63758	0.63796	0.63833	0.63871	0.63908	0.63945	0.63983	0.64020
0.36	0.64058	0.64095	0.64132	0.64170	0.64207	0.64244	0.64282	0.64319	0.64356	0.64394
0.37	0.64431	0.64468	0.64505	0.64543	0.64580	0.64617	0.64654	0.64691	0.64728	0.64766
0.38	0.64803	0.64840	0.64877	0.64914	0.64951	0.64988	0.65025	0.65062	0.65099	0.65136
0.39	0.65173	0.65210	0.65247	0.65284	0.65321	0.65358	0.65395	0.65432	0.65468	0.65505
0.40	0.65542	0.65579	0.65616	0.65653	0.65689	0.65726	0.65763	0.65800	0.65836	0.65873
0.41	0.65910	0.65946	0.65983	0.66020	0.66056	0.66093	0.66129	0.66166	0.66203	0.66239
0.42	0.66276	0.66312	0.66349	0.66385	0.66422	0.66458	0.66495	0.66531	0.66567	0.66604
0.43	0.66640	0.66677	0.66713	0.66749	0.66786	0.66822	0.66858	0.66894	0.66931	0.66967
0.44	0.67003	0.67039	0.67076	0.67112	0.67148	0.67184	0.67220	0.67256	0.67292	0.67328
0.45	0.67364	0.67401	0.67437	0.67473	0.67509	0.67545	0.67581	0.67616	0.67652	0.67688
0.46	0.67724	0.67760	0.67796	0.67832	0.67868	0.67903	0.67939	0.67975	0.68011	0.68047
0.47	0.68082	0.68118	0.68154	0.68189	0.68225	0.68261	0.68296	0.68332	0.68367	0.68403
0.48	0.68439	0.68474	0.68510	0.68545	0.68581	0.68616	0.68652	0.68687	0.68723	0.68758
0.49	0.68793	0.68829	0.68864	0.68899	0.68935	0.68970	0.69005	0.69041	0.69076	0.69111
0.50	0.69146	0.69181	0.69217	0.69252	0.69287	0.69322	0.69357	0.69392	0.69427	0.69462

Table 1K Areas under the normal curve from Z = 0.500 to 1.000.

The proportion of total area (α) under the curve that is under the portion of the curve from $-\infty$ to $\frac{x-\mu}{\sigma}$ (x represents any desired value of the variable x).

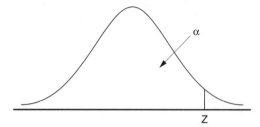

$\frac{x-\mu}{\sigma}$	0.000	0.001	0.002	0.003	0.004	0.005	0.006	0.007	0.008	0.009
0.50	0.69146	0.69181	0.69217	0.69252	0.69287	0.69322	0.69357	0.69392	0.69427	0.69462
0.51	0.69497	0.69532	0.69567	0.69602	0.69637	0.69672	0.69707	0.69742	0.69777	0.69812
0.52	0.69847	0.69882	0.69916	0.69951	0.69986	0.70021	0.70056	0.70090	0.70125	0.70160
0.53	0.70194	0.70229	0.70264	0.70298	0.70333	0.70368	0.70402	0.70437	0.70471	0.70506
0.54	0.70540	0.70575	0.70609	0.70644	0.70678	0.70712	0.70747	0.70781	0.70815	0.70850
0.55	0.70884	0.70918	0.70953	0.70987	0.71021	0.71055	0.71089	0.71124	0.71158	0.71192
0.56	0.71226	0.71260	0.71294	0.71328	0.71362	0.71396	0.71430	0.71464	0.71498	0.71532
0.57	0.71566	0.71600	0.71634	0.71668	0.71702	0.71735	0.71769	0.71803	0.71837	0.71871
0.58	0.71904	0.71938	0.71972	0.72005	0.72039	0.72073	0.72106	0.72140	0.72173	0.72207
0.59	0.72240	0.72274	0.72307	0.72341	0.72374	0.72408	0.72441	0.72475	0.72508	0.72541
0.60	0.72575	0.72608	0.72641	0.72675	0.72708	0.72741	0.72774	0.72807	0.72841	0.72874
0.61	0.72907	0.72940	0.72973	0.73006	0.73039	0.73072	0.73105	0.73138	0.73171	0.73204
0.62	0.73237	0.73270	0.73303	0.73336	0.73369	0.73401	0.73434	0.73467	0.73500	0.73533
0.63	0.73565	0.73598	0.73631	0.73663	0.73696	0.73729	0.73761	0.73794	0.73826	0.73859
0.64	0.73891	0.73924	0.73956	0.73989	0.74021	0.74054	0.74086	0.74118	0.74151	0.74183
0.65	0.74215	0.74248	0.74280	0.74312	0.74344	0.74377	0.74409	0.74441	0.74473	0.74505
0.66	0.74537	0.74569	0.74601	0.74633	0.74665	0.74697	0.74729	0.74761	0.74793	0.74825
0.67	0.74857	0.74889	0.74921	0.74953	0.74984	0.75016	0.75048	0.75080	0.75111	0.75143
0.68	0.75175	0.75206	0.75238	0.75270	0.75301	0.75333	0.75364	0.75396	0.75427	0.75459
0.69	0.75490	0.75522	0.75553	0.75585	0.75616	0.75647	0.75679	0.75710	0.75741	0.75772
0.70	0.75804	0.75835	0.75866	0.75897	0.75928	0.75959	0.75991	0.76022	0.76053	0.76084
0.71	0.76115	0.76146	0.76177	0.76208	0.76239	0.76270	0.76300	0.76331	0.76362	0.76393
0.72	0.76424	0.76455	0.76485	0.76516	0.76547	0.76577	0.76608	0.76639	0.76669	0.76700
0.73	0.76730	0.76761	0.76792	0.76822	0.76853	0.76883	0.76913	0.76944	0.76974	0.77005
0.74	0.77035	0.77065	0.77096	0.77126	0.77156	0.77186	0.77217	0.77247	0.77277	0.77307
0.75	0.77337	0.77367	0.77397	0.77428	0.77458	0.77488	0.77518	0.77548	0.77577	0.77607
0.76	0.77637	0.77667	0.77697	0.77727	0.77757	0.77786	0.77816	0.77846	0.77876	0.77905

continued

continued

$\frac{x-\mu}{\sigma}$	0.000	0.001	0.002	0.003	0.004	0.005	0.006	0.007	0.008	0.009
0.77	0.77935	0.77965	0.77994	0.78024	0.78053	0.78083	0.78113	0.78142	0.78172	0.78201
0.78	0.78230	0.78260	0.78289	0.78319	0.78348	0.78377	0.78407	0.78436	0.78465	0.78494
0.79	0.78524	0.78553	0.78582	0.78611	0.78640	0.78669	0.78698	0.78727	0.78756	0.78785
0.80	0.78814	0.78843	0.78872	0.78901	0.78930	0.78959	0.78988	0.79017	0.79045	0.79074
0.81	0.79103	0.79132	0.79160	0.79189	0.79218	0.79246	0.79275	0.79304	0.79332	0.79361
0.82	0.79389	0.79418	0.79446	0.79475	0.79503	0.79531	0.79560	0.79588	0.79616	0.79645
0.83	0.79673	0.79701	0.79730	0.79758	0.79786	0.79814	0.79842	0.79870	0.79898	0.79927
0.84	0.79955	0.79983	0.80011	0.80039	0.80067	0.80094	0.80122	0.80150	0.80178	0.80206
0.85	0.80234	0.80262	0.80289	0.80317	0.80345	0.80372	0.80400	0.80428	0.80455	0.80483
0.86	0.80511	0.80538	0.80566	0.80593	0.80621	0.80648	0.80675	0.80703	0.80730	0.80758
0.87	0.80785	0.80812	0.80840	0.80867	0.80894	0.80921	0.80948	0.80976	0.81003	0.81030
0.88	0.81057	0.81084	0.81111	0.81138	0.81165	0.81192	0.81219	0.81246	0.81273	0.81300
0.89	0.81327	0.81354	0.81380	0.81407	0.81434	0.81461	0.81487	0.81514	0.81541	0.81567
0.90	0.81594	0.81621	0.81647	0.81674	0.81700	0.81727	0.81753	0.81780	0.81806	0.81832
0.91	0.81859	0.81885	0.81912	0.81938	0.81964	0.81990	0.82017	0.82043	0.82069	0.82095
0.92	0.82121	0.82147	0.82174	0.82200	0.82226	0.82252	0.82278	0.82304	0.82330	0.82356
0.93	0.82381	0.82407	0.82433	0.82459	0.82485	0.82511	0.82536	0.82562	0.82588	0.82613
0.94	0.82639	0.82665	0.82690	0.82716	0.82742	0.82767	0.82793	0.82818	0.82844	0.82869
0.95	0.82894	0.82920	0.82945	0.82970	0.82996	0.83021	0.83046	0.83072	0.83097	0.83122
0.96	0.83147	0.83172	0.83198	0.83223	0.83248	0.83273	0.83298	0.83323	0.83348	0.83373
0.97	0.83398	0.83423	0.83447	0.83472	0.83497	0.83522	0.83547	0.83572	0.83596	0.83621
0.98	0.83646	0.83670	0.83695	0.83720	0.83744	0.83769	0.83793	0.83818	0.83842	0.83867
0.99	0.83891	0.83916	0.83940	0.83965	0.83989	0.84013	0.84037	0.84062	0.84086	0.84110
1.00	0.84134	0.84159	0.84183	0.84207	0.84231	0.84255	0.84279	0.84303	0.84327	0.84351

Table 1L   Areas under the normal curve from $Z = 1.000$ to 1.500.

The proportion of total area (α) under the curve that is under the portion of the curve from $-\infty$ to $\frac{x-\mu}{\sigma}$ (x represents any desired value of the variable x).

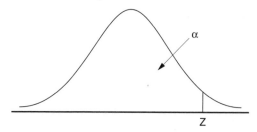

$\frac{x-\mu}{\sigma}$	0.000	0.001	0.002	0.003	0.004	0.005	0.006	0.007	0.008	0.009
1.00	0.84134	0.84159	0.84183	0.84207	0.84231	0.84255	0.84279	0.84303	0.84327	0.84351
1.01	0.84375	0.84399	0.84423	0.84447	0.84471	0.84495	0.84519	0.84542	0.84566	0.84590
1.02	0.84614	0.84637	0.84661	0.84685	0.84708	0.84732	0.84755	0.84779	0.84803	0.84826
1.03	0.84849	0.84873	0.84896	0.84920	0.84943	0.84967	0.84990	0.85013	0.85036	0.85060
1.04	0.85083	0.85106	0.85129	0.85153	0.85176	0.85199	0.85222	0.85245	0.85268	0.85291
1.05	0.85314	0.85337	0.85360	0.85383	0.85406	0.85429	0.85452	0.85474	0.85497	0.85520
1.06	0.85543	0.85566	0.85588	0.85611	0.85634	0.85656	0.85679	0.85701	0.85724	0.85747
1.07	0.85769	0.85792	0.85814	0.85836	0.85859	0.85881	0.85904	0.85926	0.85948	0.85971
1.08	0.85993	0.86015	0.86037	0.86060	0.86082	0.86104	0.86126	0.86148	0.86170	0.86192
1.09	0.86214	0.86236	0.86258	0.86280	0.86302	0.86324	0.86346	0.86368	0.86390	0.86412
1.10	0.86433	0.86455	0.86477	0.86499	0.86520	0.86542	0.86564	0.86585	0.86607	0.86628
1.11	0.86650	0.86672	0.86693	0.86715	0.86736	0.86757	0.86779	0.86800	0.86822	0.86843
1.12	0.86864	0.86886	0.86907	0.86928	0.86949	0.86971	0.86992	0.87013	0.87034	0.87055
1.13	0.87076	0.87097	0.87118	0.87139	0.87160	0.87181	0.87202	0.87223	0.87244	0.87265
1.14	0.87286	0.87307	0.87327	0.87348	0.87369	0.87390	0.87410	0.87431	0.87452	0.87472
1.15	0.87493	0.87513	0.87534	0.87554	0.87575	0.87595	0.87616	0.87636	0.87657	0.87677
1.16	0.87698	0.87718	0.87738	0.87759	0.87779	0.87799	0.87819	0.87839	0.87860	0.87880
1.17	0.87900	0.87920	0.87940	0.87960	0.87980	0.88000	0.88020	0.88040	0.88060	0.88080
1.18	0.88100	0.88120	0.88140	0.88160	0.88179	0.88199	0.88219	0.88239	0.88258	0.88278
1.19	0.88298	0.88317	0.88337	0.88357	0.88376	0.88396	0.88415	0.88435	0.88454	0.88474
1.20	0.88493	0.88512	0.88532	0.88551	0.88571	0.88590	0.88609	0.88628	0.88648	0.88667
1.21	0.88686	0.88705	0.88724	0.88744	0.88763	0.88782	0.88801	0.88820	0.88839	0.88858
1.22	0.88877	0.88896	0.88915	0.88934	0.88952	0.88971	0.88990	0.89009	0.89028	0.89046
1.23	0.89065	0.89084	0.89103	0.89121	0.89140	0.89158	0.89177	0.89196	0.89214	0.89233
1.24	0.89251	0.89270	0.89288	0.89307	0.89325	0.89343	0.89362	0.89380	0.89398	0.89417
1.25	0.89435	0.89453	0.89472	0.89490	0.89508	0.89526	0.89544	0.89562	0.89580	0.89598
1.26	0.89617	0.89635	0.89653	0.89671	0.89688	0.89706	0.89724	0.89742	0.89760	0.89778

continued

continued

$\frac{x-\mu}{\sigma}$	0.000	0.001	0.002	0.003	0.004	0.005	0.006	0.007	0.008	0.009
1.27	0.89796	0.89814	0.89831	0.89849	0.89867	0.89885	0.89902	0.89920	0.89938	0.89955
1.28	0.89973	0.89990	0.90008	0.90025	0.90043	0.90060	0.90078	0.90095	0.90113	0.90130
1.29	0.90147	0.90165	0.90182	0.90199	0.90217	0.90234	0.90251	0.90268	0.90286	0.90303
1.30	0.90320	0.90337	0.90354	0.90371	0.90388	0.90405	0.90422	0.90439	0.90456	0.90473
1.31	0.90490	0.90507	0.90524	0.90541	0.90558	0.90575	0.90591	0.90608	0.90625	0.90642
1.32	0.90658	0.90675	0.90692	0.90708	0.90725	0.90741	0.90758	0.90775	0.90791	0.90808
1.33	0.90824	0.90841	0.90857	0.90873	0.90890	0.90906	0.90923	0.90939	0.90955	0.90971
1.34	0.90988	0.91004	0.91020	0.91036	0.91053	0.91069	0.91085	0.91101	0.91117	0.91133
1.35	0.91149	0.91165	0.91181	0.91197	0.91213	0.91229	0.91245	0.91261	0.91277	0.91293
1.36	0.91309	0.91324	0.91340	0.91356	0.91372	0.91387	0.91403	0.91419	0.91434	0.91450
1.37	0.91466	0.91481	0.91497	0.91512	0.91528	0.91543	0.91559	0.91574	0.91590	0.91605
1.38	0.91621	0.91636	0.91651	0.91667	0.91682	0.91697	0.91713	0.91728	0.91743	0.91758
1.39	0.91774	0.91789	0.91804	0.91819	0.91834	0.91849	0.91864	0.91879	0.91894	0.91909
1.40	0.91924	0.91939	0.91954	0.91969	0.91984	0.91999	0.92014	0.92029	0.92043	0.92058
1.41	0.92073	0.92088	0.92103	0.92117	0.92132	0.92147	0.92161	0.92176	0.92190	0.92205
1.42	0.92220	0.92234	0.92249	0.92263	0.92278	0.92292	0.92307	0.92321	0.92335	0.92350
1.43	0.92364	0.92378	0.92393	0.92407	0.92421	0.92436	0.92450	0.92464	0.92478	0.92492
1.44	0.92507	0.92521	0.92535	0.92549	0.92563	0.92577	0.92591	0.92605	0.92619	0.92633
1.45	0.92647	0.92661	0.92675	0.92689	0.92703	0.92717	0.92730	0.92744	0.92758	0.92772
1.46	0.92785	0.92799	0.92813	0.92827	0.92840	0.92854	0.92868	0.92881	0.92895	0.92908
1.47	0.92922	0.92935	0.92949	0.92962	0.92976	0.92989	0.93003	0.93016	0.93030	0.93043
1.48	0.93056	0.93070	0.93083	0.93096	0.93110	0.93123	0.93136	0.93149	0.93162	0.93176
1.49	0.93189	0.93202	0.93215	0.93228	0.93241	0.93254	0.93267	0.93280	0.93293	0.93306
1.50	0.93319	0.93332	0.93345	0.93358	0.93371	0.93384	0.93397	0.93409	0.93422	0.93435

Table 1M Areas under the normal curve from Z = 1.500 to 2.000.

The proportion of total area (α) under the curve that is under the portion of the curve from $-\infty$ to $\frac{x-\mu}{\sigma}$ (x represents any desired value of the variable x). Note: After decimal, insert 9 before each entry.

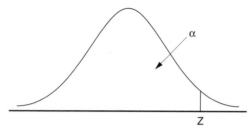

$\frac{x-\mu}{\sigma}$	0.000	0.001	0.002	0.003	0.004	0.005	0.006	0.007	0.008	0.009
1.50	0.33193	0.33322	0.33451	0.33580	0.33709	0.33838	0.33966	0.34095	0.34223	0.34351
1.51	0.34478	0.34606	0.34733	0.34860	0.34987	0.35114	0.35240	0.35367	0.35493	0.35619
1.52	0.35745	0.35870	0.35995	0.36121	0.36246	0.36370	0.36495	0.36619	0.36744	0.36868
1.53	0.36992	0.37115	0.37239	0.37362	0.37485	0.37608	0.37731	0.37853	0.37976	0.38098
1.54	0.38220	0.38342	0.38463	0.38585	0.38706	0.38827	0.38948	0.39068	0.39189	0.39309
1.55	0.39429	0.39549	0.39669	0.39788	0.39908	0.40027	0.40146	0.40265	0.40383	0.40502
1.56	0.40620	0.40738	0.40856	0.40974	0.41091	0.41209	0.41326	0.41443	0.41559	0.41676
1.57	0.41792	0.41909	0.42025	0.42141	0.42256	0.42372	0.42487	0.42602	0.42717	0.42832
1.58	0.42947	0.43061	0.43175	0.43289	0.43403	0.43517	0.43630	0.43744	0.43857	0.43970
1.59	0.44083	0.44195	0.44308	0.44420	0.44532	0.44644	0.44756	0.44867	0.44979	0.45090
1.60	0.45201	0.45312	0.45422	0.45533	0.45643	0.45753	0.45863	0.45973	0.46082	0.46192
1.61	0.46301	0.46410	0.46519	0.46628	0.46736	0.46845	0.46953	0.47061	0.47169	0.47276
1.62	0.47384	0.47491	0.47598	0.47705	0.47812	0.47919	0.48025	0.48131	0.48238	0.48343
1.63	0.48449	0.48555	0.48660	0.48766	0.48871	0.48975	0.49080	0.49185	0.49289	0.49393
1.64	0.49497	0.49601	0.49705	0.49809	0.49912	0.50015	0.50118	0.50221	0.50324	0.50426
1.65	0.50529	0.50631	0.50733	0.50835	0.50936	0.51038	0.51139	0.51240	0.51341	0.51442
1.66	0.51543	0.51643	0.51744	0.51844	0.51944	0.52044	0.52143	0.52243	0.52342	0.52441
1.67	0.52540	0.52639	0.52738	0.52836	0.52935	0.53033	0.53131	0.53229	0.53326	0.53424
1.68	0.53521	0.53619	0.53716	0.53812	0.53909	0.54006	0.54102	0.54198	0.54294	0.54390
1.69	0.54486	0.54582	0.54677	0.54772	0.54867	0.54962	0.55057	0.55152	0.55246	0.55340
1.70	0.55435	0.55529	0.55622	0.55716	0.55809	0.55903	0.55996	0.56089	0.56182	0.56275
1.71	0.56367	0.56459	0.56552	0.56644	0.56736	0.56827	0.56919	0.57010	0.57102	0.57193
1.72	0.57284	0.57375	0.57465	0.57556	0.57646	0.57736	0.57826	0.57916	0.58006	0.58095
1.73	0.58185	0.58274	0.58363	0.58452	0.58541	0.58630	0.58718	0.58806	0.58895	0.58983
1.74	0.59070	0.59158	0.59246	0.59333	0.59420	0.59508	0.59595	0.59681	0.59768	0.59854
1.75	0.59941	0.60027	0.60113	0.60199	0.60285	0.60370	0.60456	0.60541	0.60626	0.60711
1.76	0.60796	0.60881	0.60965	0.61050	0.61134	0.61218	0.61302	0.61386	0.61470	0.61553

continued

continued

$\dfrac{x-\mu}{\sigma}$	0.000	0.001	0.002	0.003	0.004	0.005	0.006	0.007	0.008	0.009
1.77	0.61636	0.61720	0.61803	0.61886	0.61968	0.62051	0.62134	0.62216	0.62298	0.62380
1.78	0.62462	0.62544	0.62625	0.62707	0.62788	0.62869	0.62950	0.63031	0.63112	0.63193
1.79	0.63273	0.63353	0.63434	0.63514	0.63593	0.63673	0.63753	0.63832	0.63911	0.63991
1.80	0.64070	0.64149	0.64227	0.64306	0.64384	0.64463	0.64541	0.64619	0.64697	0.64774
1.81	0.64852	0.64930	0.65007	0.65084	0.65161	0.65238	0.65315	0.65391	0.65468	0.65544
1.82	0.65620	0.65697	0.65773	0.65848	0.65924	0.65999	0.66075	0.66150	0.66225	0.66300
1.83	0.66375	0.66450	0.66524	0.66599	0.66673	0.66747	0.66821	0.66895	0.66969	0.67042
1.84	0.67116	0.67189	0.67262	0.67335	0.67408	0.67481	0.67554	0.67626	0.67699	0.67771
1.85	0.67843	0.67915	0.67987	0.68059	0.68130	0.68202	0.68273	0.68344	0.68415	0.68486
1.86	0.68557	0.68628	0.68698	0.68769	0.68839	0.68909	0.68979	0.69049	0.69119	0.69189
1.87	0.69258	0.69327	0.69397	0.69466	0.69535	0.69604	0.69672	0.69741	0.69809	0.69878
1.88	0.69946	0.70014	0.70082	0.70150	0.70218	0.70285	0.70353	0.70420	0.70487	0.70554
1.89	0.70621	0.70688	0.70755	0.70821	0.70887	0.70954	0.71020	0.71086	0.71152	0.71218
1.90	0.71283	0.71349	0.71414	0.71480	0.71545	0.71610	0.71675	0.71740	0.71804	0.71869
1.91	0.71933	0.71998	0.72062	0.72126	0.72190	0.72254	0.72317	0.72381	0.72444	0.72508
1.92	0.72571	0.72634	0.72697	0.72760	0.72823	0.72885	0.72948	0.73010	0.73072	0.73135
1.93	0.73197	0.73258	0.73320	0.73382	0.73443	0.73505	0.73566	0.73627	0.73688	0.73749
1.94	0.73810	0.73871	0.73931	0.73992	0.74052	0.74113	0.74173	0.74233	0.74293	0.74352
1.95	0.74412	0.74471	0.74531	0.74590	0.74649	0.74708	0.74767	0.74826	0.74885	0.74944
1.96	0.75002	0.75060	0.75119	0.75177	0.75235	0.75293	0.75351	0.75408	0.75466	0.75523
1.97	0.75581	0.75638	0.75695	0.75752	0.75809	0.75866	0.75923	0.75979	0.76036	0.76092
1.98	0.76148	0.76204	0.76260	0.76316	0.76372	0.76428	0.76483	0.76539	0.76594	0.76649
1.99	0.76705	0.76760	0.76814	0.76869	0.76924	0.76979	0.77033	0.77087	0.77142	0.77196
2.00	0.77250	0.77304	0.77358	0.77411	0.77465	0.77518	0.77572	0.77625	0.77678	0.77731

Table 1N   Areas under the normal curve from Z = 2.000 to 2.500.

The proportion of total area (α) under the curve that is under the portion of the curve from $-\infty$ to $\frac{x-\mu}{\sigma}$ (x represents any desired value of the variable x). Note: After decimal, insert 9 before each entry.

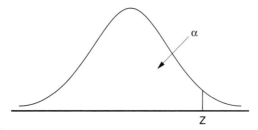

$\frac{x-\mu}{\sigma}$	0.000	0.001	0.002	0.003	0.004	0.005	0.006	0.007	0.008	0.009
2.00	0.77250	0.77304	0.77358	0.77411	0.77465	0.77518	0.77572	0.77625	0.77678	0.77731
2.01	0.77784	0.77837	0.77890	0.77943	0.77995	0.78048	0.78100	0.78152	0.78204	0.78256
2.02	0.78308	0.78360	0.78412	0.78463	0.78515	0.78566	0.78618	0.78669	0.78720	0.78771
2.03	0.78822	0.78873	0.78923	0.78974	0.79024	0.79075	0.79125	0.79175	0.79225	0.79275
2.04	0.79325	0.79375	0.79424	0.79474	0.79523	0.79573	0.79622	0.79671	0.79720	0.79769
2.05	0.79818	0.79867	0.79915	0.79964	0.80012	0.80060	0.80109	0.80157	0.80205	0.80253
2.06	0.80301	0.80348	0.80396	0.80444	0.80491	0.80538	0.80586	0.80633	0.80680	0.80727
2.07	0.80774	0.80821	0.80867	0.80914	0.80960	0.81007	0.81053	0.81099	0.81145	0.81191
2.08	0.81237	0.81283	0.81329	0.81374	0.81420	0.81465	0.81511	0.81556	0.81601	0.81646
2.09	0.81691	0.81736	0.81781	0.81825	0.81870	0.81915	0.81959	0.82003	0.82047	0.82092
2.10	0.82136	0.82180	0.82223	0.82267	0.82311	0.82354	0.82398	0.82441	0.82485	0.82528
2.11	0.82571	0.82614	0.82657	0.82700	0.82742	0.82785	0.82828	0.82870	0.82912	0.82955
2.12	0.82997	0.83039	0.83081	0.83123	0.83165	0.83207	0.83248	0.83290	0.83331	0.83373
2.13	0.83414	0.83455	0.83497	0.83538	0.83579	0.83619	0.83660	0.83701	0.83742	0.83782
2.14	0.83823	0.83863	0.83903	0.83943	0.83984	0.84024	0.84064	0.84103	0.84143	0.84183
2.15	0.84222	0.84262	0.84301	0.84341	0.84380	0.84419	0.84458	0.84497	0.84536	0.84575
2.16	0.84614	0.84652	0.84691	0.84729	0.84768	0.84806	0.84844	0.84883	0.84921	0.84959
2.17	0.84997	0.85034	0.85072	0.85110	0.85147	0.85185	0.85222	0.85260	0.85297	0.85334
2.18	0.85371	0.85408	0.85445	0.85482	0.85519	0.85556	0.85592	0.85629	0.85665	0.85702
2.19	0.85738	0.85774	0.85810	0.85846	0.85882	0.85918	0.85954	0.85990	0.86025	0.86061
2.20	0.86097	0.86132	0.86167	0.86203	0.86238	0.86273	0.86308	0.86343	0.86378	0.86413
2.21	0.86447	0.86482	0.86517	0.86551	0.86586	0.86620	0.86654	0.86688	0.86723	0.86757
2.22	0.86791	0.86825	0.86858	0.86892	0.86926	0.86959	0.86993	0.87026	0.87060	0.87093
2.23	0.87126	0.87159	0.87193	0.87226	0.87258	0.87291	0.87324	0.87357	0.87389	0.87422
2.24	0.87455	0.87487	0.87519	0.87552	0.87584	0.87616	0.87648	0.87680	0.87712	0.87744
2.25	0.87776	0.87807	0.87839	0.87870	0.87902	0.87933	0.87965	0.87996	0.88027	0.88058
2.26	0.88089	0.88120	0.88151	0.88182	0.88213	0.88244	0.88274	0.88305	0.88335	0.88366

continued

continued

$\frac{x-\mu}{\sigma}$	0.000	0.001	0.002	0.003	0.004	0.005	0.006	0.007	0.008	0.009
2.27	0.88396	0.88427	0.88457	0.88487	0.88517	0.88547	0.88577	0.88607	0.88637	0.88666
2.28	0.88696	0.88726	0.88755	0.88785	0.88814	0.88844	0.88873	0.88902	0.88931	0.88960
2.29	0.88989	0.89018	0.89047	0.89076	0.89105	0.89133	0.89162	0.89191	0.89219	0.89248
2.30	0.89276	0.89304	0.89332	0.89361	0.89389	0.89417	0.89445	0.89473	0.89500	0.89528
2.31	0.89556	0.89584	0.89611	0.89639	0.89666	0.89694	0.89721	0.89748	0.89775	0.89802
2.32	0.89830	0.89857	0.89884	0.89910	0.89937	0.89964	0.89991	0.90017	0.90044	0.90070
2.33	0.90097	0.90123	0.90150	0.90176	0.90202	0.90228	0.90254	0.90280	0.90306	0.90332
2.34	0.90358	0.90384	0.90410	0.90435	0.90461	0.90486	0.90512	0.90537	0.90563	0.90588
2.35	0.90613	0.90638	0.90664	0.90689	0.90714	0.90739	0.90764	0.90788	0.90813	0.90838
2.36	0.90863	0.90887	0.90912	0.90936	0.90961	0.90985	0.91009	0.91034	0.91058	0.91082
2.37	0.91106	0.91130	0.91154	0.91178	0.91202	0.91226	0.91249	0.91273	0.91297	0.91320
2.38	0.91344	0.91367	0.91391	0.91414	0.91437	0.91460	0.91484	0.91507	0.91530	0.91553
2.39	0.91576	0.91599	0.91622	0.91644	0.91667	0.91690	0.91712	0.91735	0.91758	0.91780
2.40	0.91802	0.91825	0.91847	0.91869	0.91892	0.91914	0.91936	0.91958	0.91980	0.92002
2.41	0.92024	0.92046	0.92067	0.92089	0.92111	0.92132	0.92154	0.92175	0.92197	0.92218
2.42	0.92240	0.92261	0.92282	0.92304	0.92325	0.92346	0.92367	0.92388	0.92409	0.92430
2.43	0.92451	0.92471	0.92492	0.92513	0.92534	0.92554	0.92575	0.92595	0.92616	0.92636
2.44	0.92656	0.92677	0.92697	0.92717	0.92737	0.92757	0.92777	0.92797	0.92817	0.92837
2.45	0.92857	0.92877	0.92897	0.92916	0.92936	0.92956	0.92975	0.92995	0.93014	0.93034
2.46	0.93053	0.93072	0.93092	0.93111	0.93130	0.93149	0.93168	0.93187	0.93206	0.93225
2.47	0.93244	0.93263	0.93282	0.93301	0.93320	0.93338	0.93357	0.93375	0.93394	0.93412
2.48	0.93431	0.93449	0.93468	0.93486	0.93504	0.93522	0.93541	0.93559	0.93577	0.93595
2.49	0.93613	0.93631	0.93649	0.93667	0.93684	0.93702	0.93720	0.93738	0.93755	0.93773
2.50	0.93790	0.93808	0.93825	0.93843	0.93860	0.93877	0.93895	0.93912	0.93929	0.93946

Table 10 Areas under the normal curve from $Z = 2.500$ to 3.000.

The proportion of total area (α) under the curve that is under the portion of the curve from $-\infty$ to $\dfrac{x - \mu}{\sigma}$ (x represents any desired value of the variable x). Note: After decimal, insert 99 before each entry.

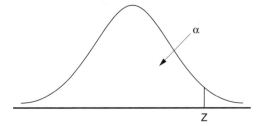

$\dfrac{x - \mu}{\sigma}$	0.000	0.001	0.002	0.003	0.004	0.005	0.006	0.007	0.008	0.009
2.50	0.37903	0.38078	0.38253	0.38427	0.38601	0.38774	0.38947	0.39120	0.39292	0.39463
2.51	0.39634	0.39805	0.39975	0.40145	0.40315	0.40484	0.40652	0.40821	0.40988	0.41156
2.52	0.41323	0.41489	0.41655	0.41821	0.41986	0.42151	0.42315	0.42479	0.42643	0.42806
2.53	0.42969	0.43131	0.43293	0.43455	0.43616	0.43776	0.43937	0.44097	0.44256	0.44415
2.54	0.44574	0.44732	0.44890	0.45047	0.45204	0.45361	0.45517	0.45673	0.45829	0.45984
2.55	0.46139	0.46293	0.46447	0.46600	0.46753	0.46906	0.47058	0.47210	0.47362	0.47513
2.56	0.47664	0.47814	0.47964	0.48114	0.48263	0.48412	0.48561	0.48709	0.48856	0.49004
2.57	0.49151	0.49297	0.49444	0.49589	0.49735	0.49880	0.50025	0.50169	0.50313	0.50457
2.58	0.50600	0.50743	0.50885	0.51027	0.51169	0.51311	0.51452	0.51592	0.51733	0.51872
2.59	0.52012	0.52151	0.52290	0.52429	0.52567	0.52705	0.52842	0.52979	0.53116	0.53252
2.60	0.53388	0.53524	0.53659	0.53794	0.53929	0.54063	0.54197	0.54330	0.54464	0.54596
2.61	0.54729	0.54861	0.54993	0.55124	0.55255	0.55386	0.55517	0.55647	0.55777	0.55906
2.62	0.56035	0.56164	0.56292	0.56420	0.56548	0.56676	0.56803	0.56929	0.57056	0.57182
2.63	0.57308	0.57433	0.57558	0.57683	0.57807	0.57931	0.58055	0.58179	0.58302	0.58425
2.64	0.58547	0.58669	0.58791	0.58912	0.59034	0.59155	0.59275	0.59395	0.59515	0.59635
2.65	0.59754	0.59873	0.59992	0.60110	0.60228	0.60346	0.60463	0.60580	0.60697	0.60814
2.66	0.60930	0.61046	0.61161	0.61276	0.61391	0.61506	0.61620	0.61734	0.61848	0.61961
2.67	0.62074	0.62187	0.62300	0.62412	0.62524	0.62635	0.62747	0.62858	0.62968	0.63079
2.68	0.63189	0.63299	0.63408	0.63518	0.63626	0.63735	0.63843	0.63952	0.64059	0.64167
2.69	0.64274	0.64381	0.64488	0.64594	0.64700	0.64806	0.64911	0.65016	0.65121	0.65226
2.70	0.65330	0.65434	0.65538	0.65642	0.65745	0.65848	0.65950	0.66053	0.66155	0.66257
2.71	0.66358	0.66460	0.66561	0.66661	0.66762	0.66862	0.66962	0.67062	0.67161	0.67260
2.72	0.67359	0.67458	0.67556	0.67654	0.67752	0.67849	0.67947	0.68043	0.68140	0.68237
2.73	0.68333	0.68429	0.68524	0.68620	0.68715	0.68810	0.68904	0.68999	0.69093	0.69187
2.74	0.69280	0.69374	0.69467	0.69560	0.69652	0.69745	0.69837	0.69928	0.70020	0.70111
2.75	0.70202	0.70293	0.70384	0.70474	0.70564	0.70654	0.70744	0.70833	0.70922	0.71011
2.76	0.71099	0.71188	0.71276	0.71364	0.71451	0.71539	0.71626	0.71713	0.71799	0.71886

continued

continued

$\frac{x-\mu}{\sigma}$	0.000	0.001	0.002	0.003	0.004	0.005	0.006	0.007	0.008	0.009
2.77	0.71972	0.72058	0.72143	0.72229	0.72314	0.72399	0.72484	0.72568	0.72653	0.72737
2.78	0.72821	0.72904	0.72987	0.73071	0.73153	0.73236	0.73319	0.73401	0.73483	0.73564
2.79	0.73646	0.73727	0.73808	0.73889	0.73970	0.74050	0.74130	0.74210	0.74290	0.74369
2.80	0.74449	0.74528	0.74607	0.74685	0.74764	0.74842	0.74920	0.74997	0.75075	0.75152
2.81	0.75229	0.75306	0.75383	0.75459	0.75535	0.75611	0.75687	0.75763	0.75838	0.75913
2.82	0.75988	0.76063	0.76137	0.76212	0.76286	0.76360	0.76433	0.76507	0.76580	0.76653
2.83	0.76726	0.76799	0.76871	0.76943	0.77015	0.77087	0.77159	0.77230	0.77301	0.77372
2.84	0.77443	0.77514	0.77584	0.77654	0.77724	0.77794	0.77864	0.77933	0.78003	0.78072
2.85	0.78140	0.78209	0.78277	0.78346	0.78414	0.78482	0.78549	0.78617	0.78684	0.78751
2.86	0.78818	0.78885	0.78951	0.79017	0.79084	0.79150	0.79215	0.79281	0.79346	0.79411
2.87	0.79476	0.79541	0.79606	0.79670	0.79735	0.79799	0.79863	0.79926	0.79990	0.80053
2.88	0.80116	0.80179	0.80242	0.80305	0.80367	0.80429	0.80491	0.80553	0.80615	0.80677
2.89	0.80738	0.80799	0.80860	0.80921	0.80982	0.81042	0.81102	0.81163	0.81222	0.81282
2.90	0.81342	0.81401	0.81461	0.81520	0.81579	0.81637	0.81696	0.81754	0.81813	0.81871
2.91	0.81929	0.81986	0.82044	0.82101	0.82159	0.82216	0.82272	0.82329	0.82386	0.82442
2.92	0.82498	0.82555	0.82610	0.82666	0.82722	0.82777	0.82832	0.82888	0.82942	0.82997
2.93	0.83052	0.83106	0.83161	0.83215	0.83269	0.83323	0.83376	0.83430	0.83483	0.83536
2.94	0.83589	0.83642	0.83695	0.83748	0.83800	0.83852	0.83904	0.83956	0.84008	0.84060
2.95	0.84111	0.84163	0.84214	0.84265	0.84316	0.84367	0.84417	0.84468	0.84518	0.84568
2.96	0.84618	0.84668	0.84718	0.84767	0.84817	0.84866	0.84915	0.84964	0.85013	0.85061
2.97	0.85110	0.85158	0.85207	0.85255	0.85303	0.85351	0.85398	0.85446	0.85493	0.85540
2.98	0.85588	0.85635	0.85681	0.85728	0.85775	0.85821	0.85867	0.85914	0.85960	0.86005
2.99	0.86051	0.86097	0.86142	0.86188	0.86233	0.86278	0.86323	0.86367	0.86412	0.86457
3.00	0.86501	0.86545	0.86589	0.86633	0.86677	0.86721	0.86765	0.86808	0.86851	0.86895

Table 1P Areas under the normal curve from Z = 3.000 to 3.500.

The proportion of total area (α) under the curve that is under the portion of the curve from $-\infty$ to $\frac{x-\mu}{\sigma}$ (x represents any desired value of the variable x). Note: After decimal, insert 99 before each entry.

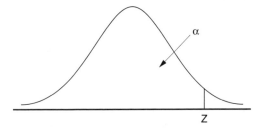

$\frac{x-\mu}{\sigma}$	0.000	0.001	0.002	0.003	0.004	0.005	0.006	0.007	0.008	0.009
3.00	0.86501	0.86545	0.86589	0.86633	0.86677	0.86721	0.86765	0.86808	0.86851	0.86895
3.01	0.86938	0.86981	0.87023	0.87066	0.87109	0.87151	0.87193	0.87236	0.87278	0.87319
3.02	0.87361	0.87403	0.87444	0.87486	0.87527	0.87568	0.87609	0.87650	0.87691	0.87732
3.03	0.87772	0.87813	0.87853	0.87893	0.87933	0.87973	0.88013	0.88053	0.88092	0.88132
3.04	0.88171	0.88210	0.88249	0.88288	0.88327	0.88366	0.88405	0.88443	0.88482	0.88520
3.05	0.88558	0.88596	0.88634	0.88672	0.88709	0.88747	0.88784	0.88822	0.88859	0.88896
3.06	0.88933	0.88970	0.89007	0.89043	0.89080	0.89117	0.89153	0.89189	0.89225	0.89261
3.07	0.89297	0.89333	0.89369	0.89404	0.89440	0.89475	0.89510	0.89545	0.89580	0.89615
3.08	0.89650	0.89685	0.89719	0.89754	0.89788	0.89822	0.89857	0.89891	0.89925	0.89958
3.09	0.89992	0.90026	0.90059	0.90093	0.90126	0.90159	0.90192	0.90226	0.90258	0.90291
3.10	0.90324	0.90357	0.90389	0.90422	0.90454	0.90486	0.90518	0.90550	0.90582	0.90614
3.11	0.90646	0.90677	0.90709	0.90740	0.90772	0.90803	0.90834	0.90865	0.90896	0.90927
3.12	0.90957	0.90988	0.91019	0.91049	0.91079	0.91110	0.91140	0.91170	0.91200	0.91230
3.13	0.91260	0.91289	0.91319	0.91349	0.91378	0.91407	0.91437	0.91466	0.91495	0.91524
3.14	0.91553	0.91581	0.91610	0.91639	0.91667	0.91696	0.91724	0.91752	0.91780	0.91808
3.15	0.91836	0.91864	0.91892	0.91920	0.91948	0.91975	0.92003	0.92030	0.92057	0.92084
3.16	0.92112	0.92139	0.92166	0.92192	0.92219	0.92246	0.92272	0.92299	0.92325	0.92352
3.17	0.92378	0.92404	0.92430	0.92456	0.92482	0.92508	0.92534	0.92560	0.92585	0.92611
3.18	0.92636	0.92662	0.92687	0.92712	0.92737	0.92762	0.92787	0.92812	0.92837	0.92862
3.19	0.92886	0.92911	0.92935	0.92960	0.92984	0.93008	0.93033	0.93057	0.93081	0.93105
3.20	0.93129	0.93152	0.93176	0.93200	0.93223	0.93247	0.93270	0.93294	0.93317	0.93340
3.21	0.93363	0.93386	0.93409	0.93432	0.93455	0.93478	0.93500	0.93523	0.93546	0.93568
3.22	0.93590	0.93613	0.93635	0.93657	0.93679	0.93701	0.93723	0.93745	0.93767	0.93789
3.23	0.93810	0.93832	0.93854	0.93875	0.93897	0.93918	0.93939	0.93960	0.93981	0.94003
3.24	0.94024	0.94044	0.94065	0.94086	0.94107	0.94127	0.94148	0.94169	0.94189	0.94209
3.25	0.94230	0.94250	0.94270	0.94290	0.94310	0.94330	0.94350	0.94370	0.94390	0.94410
3.26	0.94429	0.94449	0.94469	0.94488	0.94507	0.94527	0.94546	0.94565	0.94584	0.94604

continued

continued

$\dfrac{x-\mu}{\sigma}$	0.000	0.001	0.002	0.003	0.004	0.005	0.006	0.007	0.008	0.009
3.27	0.94623	0.94642	0.94661	0.94679	0.94698	0.94717	0.94736	0.94754	0.94773	0.94791
3.28	0.94810	0.94828	0.94846	0.94865	0.94883	0.94901	0.94919	0.94937	0.94955	0.94973
3.29	0.94991	0.95008	0.95026	0.95044	0.95061	0.95079	0.95096	0.95114	0.95131	0.95149
3.30	0.95166	0.95183	0.95200	0.95217	0.95234	0.95251	0.95268	0.95285	0.95302	0.95319
3.31	0.95335	0.95352	0.95368	0.95385	0.95401	0.95418	0.95434	0.95451	0.95467	0.95483
3.32	0.95499	0.95515	0.95531	0.95547	0.95563	0.95579	0.95595	0.95611	0.95626	0.95642
3.33	0.95658	0.95673	0.95689	0.95704	0.95720	0.95735	0.95750	0.95766	0.95781	0.95796
3.34	0.95811	0.95826	0.95841	0.95856	0.95871	0.95886	0.95901	0.95915	0.95930	0.95945
3.35	0.95959	0.95974	0.95988	0.96003	0.96017	0.96032	0.96046	0.96060	0.96075	0.96089
3.36	0.96103	0.96117	0.96131	0.96145	0.96159	0.96173	0.96187	0.96200	0.96214	0.96228
3.37	0.96242	0.96255	0.96269	0.96282	0.96296	0.96309	0.96323	0.96336	0.96349	0.96362
3.38	0.96376	0.96389	0.96402	0.96415	0.96428	0.96441	0.96454	0.96467	0.96480	0.96493
3.39	0.96505	0.96518	0.96531	0.96543	0.96556	0.96569	0.96581	0.96594	0.96606	0.96618
3.40	0.96631	0.96643	0.96655	0.96667	0.96680	0.96692	0.96704	0.96716	0.96728	0.96740
3.41	0.96752	0.96764	0.96776	0.96787	0.96799	0.96811	0.96823	0.96834	0.96846	0.96857
3.42	0.96869	0.96880	0.96892	0.96903	0.96915	0.96926	0.96937	0.96949	0.96960	0.96971
3.43	0.96982	0.96993	0.97004	0.97015	0.97026	0.97037	0.97048	0.97059	0.97070	0.97081
3.44	0.97091	0.97102	0.97113	0.97124	0.97134	0.97145	0.97155	0.97166	0.97176	0.97187
3.45	0.97197	0.97207	0.97218	0.97228	0.97238	0.97249	0.97259	0.97269	0.97279	0.97289
3.46	0.97299	0.97309	0.97319	0.97329	0.97339	0.97349	0.97359	0.97368	0.97378	0.97388
3.47	0.97398	0.97407	0.97417	0.97427	0.97436	0.97446	0.97455	0.97465	0.97474	0.97484
3.48	0.97493	0.97502	0.97512	0.97521	0.97530	0.97539	0.97548	0.97558	0.97567	0.97576
3.49	0.97585	0.97594	0.97603	0.97612	0.97621	0.97630	0.97639	0.97647	0.97656	0.97665
3.50	0.97674	0.97682	0.97691	0.97700	0.97708	0.97717	0.97726	0.97734	0.97743	0.97751

Table 1Q Areas under the normal curve from $Z = 3.500$ to 4.000.

The proportion of total area (α) under the curve that is under the portion of the curve from $-\infty$ to $\frac{x-\mu}{\sigma}$ (x represents any desired value of the variable x). Note: After decimal, insert 999 before each entry.

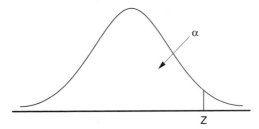

$\frac{x-\mu}{\sigma}$	0.000	0.001	0.002	0.003	0.004	0.005	0.006	0.007	0.008	0.009
3.50	0.76737	0.76824	0.76911	0.76998	0.77084	0.77170	0.77255	0.77341	0.77426	0.77510
3.51	0.77595	0.77679	0.77763	0.77846	0.77929	0.78012	0.78095	0.78177	0.78259	0.78341
3.52	0.78423	0.78504	0.78585	0.78665	0.78746	0.78826	0.78906	0.78985	0.79064	0.79143
3.53	0.79222	0.79300	0.79379	0.79456	0.79534	0.79611	0.79688	0.79765	0.79841	0.79918
3.54	0.79994	0.80069	0.80145	0.80220	0.80295	0.80369	0.80444	0.80518	0.80592	0.80665
3.55	0.80738	0.80811	0.80884	0.80957	0.81029	0.81101	0.81173	0.81244	0.81316	0.81387
3.56	0.81457	0.81528	0.81598	0.81668	0.81738	0.81807	0.81876	0.81945	0.82014	0.82083
3.57	0.82151	0.82219	0.82287	0.82354	0.82422	0.82489	0.82555	0.82622	0.82688	0.82754
3.58	0.82820	0.82886	0.82951	0.83016	0.83081	0.83146	0.83211	0.83275	0.83339	0.83403
3.59	0.83466	0.83529	0.83593	0.83655	0.83718	0.83780	0.83843	0.83905	0.83966	0.84028
3.60	0.84089	0.84150	0.84211	0.84272	0.84332	0.84392	0.84452	0.84512	0.84572	0.84631
3.61	0.84690	0.84749	0.84808	0.84866	0.84925	0.84983	0.85040	0.85098	0.85156	0.85213
3.62	0.85270	0.85327	0.85383	0.85440	0.85496	0.85552	0.85608	0.85663	0.85719	0.85774
3.63	0.85829	0.85884	0.85938	0.85993	0.86047	0.86101	0.86155	0.86208	0.86262	0.86315
3.64	0.86368	0.86421	0.86474	0.86526	0.86578	0.86630	0.86682	0.86734	0.86786	0.86837
3.65	0.86888	0.86939	0.86990	0.87040	0.87091	0.87141	0.87191	0.87241	0.87290	0.87340
3.66	0.87389	0.87438	0.87487	0.87536	0.87585	0.87633	0.87681	0.87729	0.87777	0.87825
3.67	0.87872	0.87920	0.87967	0.88014	0.88061	0.88108	0.88154	0.88200	0.88247	0.88292
3.68	0.88338	0.88384	0.88429	0.88475	0.88520	0.88565	0.88610	0.88654	0.88699	0.88743
3.69	0.88787	0.88831	0.88875	0.88919	0.88962	0.89006	0.89049	0.89092	0.89135	0.89177
3.70	0.89220	0.89262	0.89305	0.89347	0.89389	0.89430	0.89472	0.89514	0.89555	0.89596
3.71	0.89637	0.89678	0.89719	0.89759	0.89800	0.89840	0.89880	0.89920	0.89960	0.89999
3.72	0.90039	0.90078	0.90117	0.90157	0.90195	0.90234	0.90273	0.90311	0.90350	0.90388
3.73	0.90426	0.90464	0.90502	0.90539	0.90577	0.90614	0.90651	0.90689	0.90726	0.90762
3.74	0.90799	0.90836	0.90872	0.90908	0.90944	0.90980	0.91016	0.91052	0.91087	0.91123
3.75	0.91158	0.91193	0.91229	0.91263	0.91298	0.91333	0.91367	0.91402	0.91436	0.91470
3.76	0.91504	0.91538	0.91572	0.91606	0.91639	0.91673	0.91706	0.91739	0.91772	0.91805

continued

continued

$\dfrac{x-\mu}{\sigma}$	0.000	0.001	0.002	0.003	0.004	0.005	0.006	0.007	0.008	0.009
3.77	0.91838	0.91870	0.91903	0.91935	0.91967	0.92000	0.92032	0.92064	0.92095	0.92127
3.78	0.92159	0.92190	0.92221	0.92253	0.92284	0.92315	0.92345	0.92376	0.92407	0.92437
3.79	0.92468	0.92498	0.92528	0.92558	0.92588	0.92618	0.92648	0.92677	0.92707	0.92736
3.80	0.92765	0.92794	0.92823	0.92852	0.92881	0.92910	0.92938	0.92967	0.92995	0.93024
3.81	0.93052	0.93080	0.93108	0.93135	0.93163	0.93191	0.93218	0.93246	0.93273	0.93300
3.82	0.93327	0.93354	0.93381	0.93408	0.93435	0.93461	0.93488	0.93514	0.93541	0.93567
3.83	0.93593	0.93619	0.93645	0.93671	0.93696	0.93722	0.93747	0.93773	0.93798	0.93823
3.84	0.93848	0.93873	0.93898	0.93923	0.93948	0.93972	0.93997	0.94021	0.94046	0.94070
3.85	0.94094	0.94118	0.94142	0.94166	0.94190	0.94214	0.94237	0.94261	0.94284	0.94307
3.86	0.94331	0.94354	0.94377	0.94400	0.94423	0.94446	0.94468	0.94491	0.94513	0.94536
3.87	0.94558	0.94581	0.94603	0.94625	0.94647	0.94669	0.94691	0.94712	0.94734	0.94756
3.88	0.94777	0.94799	0.94820	0.94841	0.94862	0.94884	0.94905	0.94925	0.94946	0.94967
3.89	0.94988	0.95008	0.95029	0.95049	0.95070	0.95090	0.95110	0.95130	0.95150	0.95170
3.90	0.95190	0.95210	0.95230	0.95250	0.95269	0.95289	0.95308	0.95328	0.95347	0.95366
3.91	0.95385	0.95404	0.95423	0.95442	0.95461	0.95480	0.95498	0.95517	0.95536	0.95554
3.92	0.95573	0.95591	0.95609	0.95627	0.95645	0.95664	0.95681	0.95699	0.95717	0.95735
3.93	0.95753	0.95770	0.95788	0.95805	0.95823	0.95840	0.95857	0.95875	0.95892	0.95909
3.94	0.95926	0.95943	0.95960	0.95977	0.95993	0.96010	0.96027	0.96043	0.96060	0.96076
3.95	0.96092	0.96109	0.96125	0.96141	0.96157	0.96173	0.96189	0.96205	0.96221	0.96237
3.96	0.96253	0.96268	0.96284	0.96299	0.96315	0.96330	0.96346	0.96361	0.96376	0.96391
3.97	0.96406	0.96421	0.96436	0.96451	0.96466	0.96481	0.96496	0.96510	0.96525	0.96540
3.98	0.96554	0.96569	0.96583	0.96597	0.96612	0.96626	0.96640	0.96654	0.96668	0.96682
3.99	0.96696	0.96710	0.96724	0.96738	0.96752	0.96765	0.96779	0.96792	0.96806	0.96819
4.00	0.96833	0.96846	0.96860	0.96873	0.96886	0.96899	0.96912	0.96925	0.96938	0.96951

Table 2 Percentage points, student's *t* distribution (upper tail probabilities).

For a given ν (degrees of freedom), this table gives the critical values of the *t* distribution so that the proportion of the curve to the right of the critical value is α.

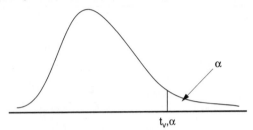

$t_{\nu,\alpha}$

	α 0.25	0.10	0.05	0.025	0.010	0.005	0.0005
ν	2 α 0.50	0.20	0.10	0.050	0.020	0.010	0.0010
1	1.00000	3.07768	6.31375	12.70620	31.82052	63.65674	636.61925
2	0.81650	1.88562	2.91999	4.30265	6.96456	9.92484	31.59905
3	0.76489	1.63774	2.35336	3.18245	4.54070	5.84091	12.92398
4	0.74070	1.53321	2.13185	2.77645	3.74695	4.60409	8.61030
5	0.72669	1.47588	2.01505	2.57058	3.36493	4.03214	6.86883
6	0.71756	1.43976	1.94318	2.44691	3.14267	3.70743	5.95882
7	0.71114	1.41492	1.89458	2.36462	2.99795	3.49948	5.40788
8	0.70639	1.39682	1.85955	2.30600	2.89646	3.35539	5.04131
9	0.70272	1.38303	1.83311	2.26216	2.82144	3.24984	4.78091
10	0.69981	1.37218	1.81246	2.22814	2.76377	3.16927	4.58689
11	0.69745	1.36343	1.79588	2.20099	2.71808	3.10581	4.43698
12	0.69548	1.35622	1.78229	2.17881	2.68100	3.05454	4.31779
13	0.69383	1.35017	1.77093	2.16037	2.65031	3.01228	4.22083
14	0.69242	1.34503	1.76131	2.14479	2.62449	2.97684	4.14045
15	0.69120	1.34061	1.75305	2.13145	2.60248	2.94671	4.07277
16	0.69013	1.33676	1.74588	2.11991	2.58349	2.92078	4.01500
17	0.68920	1.33338	1.73961	2.10982	2.56693	2.89823	3.96513
18	0.68836	1.33039	1.73406	2.10092	2.55238	2.87844	3.92165
19	0.68762	1.32773	1.72913	2.09302	2.53948	2.86093	3.88341
20	0.68695	1.32534	1.72472	2.08596	2.52798	2.84534	3.84952
21	0.68635	1.32319	1.72074	2.07961	2.51765	2.83136	3.81928
22	0.68581	1.32124	1.71714	2.07387	2.50832	2.81876	3.79213
23	0.68531	1.31946	1.71387	2.06866	2.49987	2.80734	3.76763
24	0.68485	1.31784	1.71088	2.06390	2.49216	2.79694	3.74540
25	0.68443	1.31635	1.70814	2.05954	2.48511	2.78744	3.72514
26	0.68404	1.31497	1.70562	2.05553	2.47863	2.77871	3.70661
27	0.68368	1.31370	1.70329	2.05183	2.47266	2.77068	3.68959

continued

continued

ν	α 0.25 2 α 0.50	0.10 0.20	0.05 0.10	0.025 0.050	0.010 0.020	0.005 0.010	0.0005 0.0010
28	0.68335	1.31253	1.70113	2.04841	2.46714	2.76326	3.67391
29	0.68304	1.31143	1.69913	2.04523	2.46202	2.75639	3.65941
30	0.68276	1.31042	1.69726	2.04227	2.45726	2.75000	3.64596
32	0.68223	1.30857	1.69389	2.03693	2.44868	2.73848	3.62180
34	0.68177	1.30695	1.69092	2.03224	2.44115	2.72839	3.60072
36	0.68137	1.30551	1.68830	2.02809	2.43449	2.71948	3.58215
38	0.68100	1.30423	1.68595	2.02439	2.42857	2.71156	3.56568
40	0.68067	1.30308	1.68385	2.02108	2.42326	2.70446	3.55097
45	0.67998	1.30065	1.67943	2.01410	2.41212	2.68959	3.52025
50	0.67943	1.29871	1.67591	2.00856	2.40327	2.67779	3.49601
55	0.67898	1.29713	1.67303	2.00404	2.39608	2.66822	3.47640
60	0.67860	1.29582	1.67065	2.00030	2.39012	2.66028	3.46020
70	0.67801	1.29376	1.66691	1.99444	2.38081	2.64790	3.43501
80	0.67757	1.29222	1.66412	1.99006	2.37387	2.63869	3.41634
100	0.67695	1.29007	1.66023	1.98397	2.36422	2.62589	3.39049
120	0.67654	1.28865	1.65765	1.97993	2.35782	2.61742	3.37345
∞	0.67449	1.28155	1.64485	1.95996	2.32635	2.57583	3.29053

Table 3A Critical values of the *F* distribution with numerator and denominator degrees of freedom for α = .10.

For a given numerator and denominator degrees of freedom, this table gives the critical value of the F distribution so that the proportion of the curve to the right of that critical value is α.

Note: $F_{dfn, dfd, \alpha} = 1/F_{dfd, dfn, 1-\alpha}$

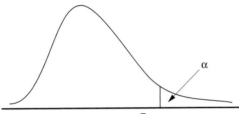

$F_{dfn, \ dfd, \alpha}$

dfd	dfn									
	1	2	3	4	5	6	7	8	9	10
1	39.86	49.50	53.59	55.83	57.24	58.20	58.91	59.44	59.86	60.19
2	8.53	9.00	9.16	9.24	9.29	9.33	9.35	9.37	9.38	9.39
3	5.54	5.46	5.39	5.34	5.31	5.28	5.27	5.25	5.24	5.23
4	4.54	4.32	4.19	4.11	4.05	4.01	3.98	3.95	3.94	3.92
5	4.06	3.78	3.62	3.52	3.45	3.40	3.37	3.34	3.32	3.30
6	3.78	3.46	3.29	3.18	3.11	3.05	3.01	2.98	2.96	2.94
7	3.59	3.26	3.07	2.96	2.88	2.83	2.78	2.75	2.72	2.70
8	3.46	3.11	2.92	2.81	2.73	2.67	2.62	2.59	2.56	2.54
9	3.36	3.01	2.81	2.69	2.61	2.55	2.51	2.47	2.44	2.42
10	3.29	2.92	2.73	2.61	2.52	2.46	2.41	2.38	2.35	2.32
11	3.23	2.86	2.66	2.54	2.45	2.39	2.34	2.30	2.27	2.25
12	3.18	2.81	2.61	2.48	2.39	2.33	2.28	2.24	2.21	2.19
13	3.14	2.76	2.56	2.43	2.35	2.28	2.23	2.20	2.16	2.14
14	3.10	2.73	2.52	2.39	2.31	2.24	2.19	2.15	2.12	2.10
15	3.07	2.70	2.49	2.36	2.27	2.21	2.16	2.12	2.09	2.06
16	3.05	2.67	2.46	2.33	2.24	2.18	2.13	2.09	2.06	2.03
17	3.03	2.64	2.44	2.31	2.22	2.15	2.10	2.06	2.03	2.00
18	3.01	2.62	2.42	2.29	2.20	2.13	2.08	2.04	2.00	1.98
19	2.99	2.61	2.40	2.27	2.18	2.11	2.06	2.02	1.98	1.96
20	2.97	2.59	2.38	2.25	2.16	2.09	2.04	2.00	1.96	1.94
25	2.92	2.53	2.32	2.18	2.09	2.02	1.97	1.93	1.89	1.87
30	2.88	2.49	2.28	2.14	2.05	1.98	1.93	1.88	1.85	1.82
35	2.85	2.46	2.25	2.11	2.02	1.95	1.90	1.85	1.82	1.79
40	2.84	2.44	2.23	2.09	2.00	1.93	1.87	1.83	1.79	1.76

continued

continued

dfd	dfn									
	1	**2**	**3**	**4**	**5**	**6**	**7**	**8**	**9**	**10**
45	2.82	2.42	2.21	2.07	1.98	1.91	1.85	1.81	1.77	1.74
50	2.81	2.41	2.20	2.06	1.97	1.90	1.84	1.80	1.76	1.73
60	2.79	2.39	2.18	2.04	1.95	1.87	1.82	1.77	1.74	1.71
70	2.78	2.38	2.16	2.03	1.93	1.86	1.80	1.76	1.72	1.69
80	2.77	2.37	2.15	2.02	1.92	1.85	1.79	1.75	1.71	1.68
90	2.76	2.36	2.15	2.01	1.91	1.84	1.78	1.74	1.70	1.67
100	2.76	2.36	2.14	2.00	1.91	1.83	1.78	1.73	1.69	1.66
150	2.74	2.34	2.12	1.98	1.89	1.81	1.76	1.71	1.67	1.64
200	2.73	2.33	2.11	1.97	1.88	1.80	1.75	1.70	1.66	1.63
500	2.72	2.31	2.09	1.96	1.86	1.79	1.73	1.68	1.64	1.61
1000	2.71	2.31	2.09	1.95	1.85	1.78	1.72	1.68	1.64	1.61
∞	2.71	2.30	2.08	1.94	1.85	1.77	1.72	1.67	1.63	1.60

Table 3B Critical values of the *F* distribution with numerator and denominator degrees of freedom for α = .10.

For a given numerator and denominator degrees of freedom, this table gives the critical value of the F distribution so that the proportion of the curve to the right of that critical value is α.

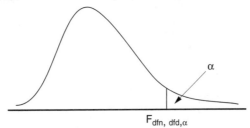

$F_{\text{dfn, dfd},\alpha}$

						dfn							
dfd	**11**	**12**	**13**	**14**	**15**	**20**	**25**	**30**	**40**	**50**	**75**	**100**	**∞**
1	60.47	60.71	60.90	61.07	61.22	61.74	62.05	62.26	62.53	62.69	62.90	63.01	63.33
2	9.40	9.41	9.41	9.42	9.42	9.44	9.45	9.46	9.47	9.47	9.48	9.48	9.49
3	5.22	5.22	5.21	5.20	5.20	5.18	5.17	5.17	5.16	5.15	5.15	5.14	5.13
4	3.91	3.90	3.89	3.88	3.87	3.84	3.83	3.82	3.80	3.80	3.78	3.78	3.76
5	3.28	3.27	3.26	3.25	3.24	3.21	3.19	3.17	3.16	3.15	3.13	3.13	3.11
6	2.92	2.90	2.89	2.88	2.87	2.84	2.81	2.80	2.78	2.77	2.75	2.75	2.72
7	2.68	2.67	2.65	2.64	2.63	2.59	2.57	2.56	2.54	2.52	2.51	2.50	2.47
8	2.52	2.50	2.49	2.48	2.46	2.42	2.40	2.38	2.36	2.35	2.33	2.32	2.30
9	2.40	2.38	2.36	2.35	2.34	2.30	2.27	2.25	2.23	2.22	2.20	2.19	2.16
10	2.30	2.28	2.27	2.26	2.24	2.20	2.17	2.16	2.13	2.12	2.10	2.09	2.06
11	2.23	2.21	2.19	2.18	2.17	2.12	2.10	2.08	2.05	2.04	2.02	2.01	1.97
12	2.17	2.15	2.13	2.12	2.10	2.06	2.03	2.01	1.99	1.97	1.95	1.94	1.90
13	2.12	2.10	2.08	2.07	2.05	2.01	1.98	1.96	1.93	1.92	1.89	1.88	1.85
14	2.07	2.05	2.04	2.02	2.01	1.96	1.93	1.91	1.89	1.87	1.85	1.83	1.80
15	2.04	2.02	2.00	1.99	1.97	1.92	1.89	1.87	1.85	1.83	1.80	1.79	1.76
16	2.01	1.99	1.97	1.95	1.94	1.89	1.86	1.84	1.81	1.79	1.77	1.76	1.72
17	1.98	1.96	1.94	1.93	1.91	1.86	1.83	1.81	1.78	1.76	1.74	1.73	1.69
18	1.95	1.93	1.92	1.90	1.89	1.84	1.80	1.78	1.75	1.74	1.71	1.70	1.66
19	1.93	1.91	1.89	1.88	1.86	1.81	1.78	1.76	1.73	1.71	1.69	1.67	1.63
20	1.91	1.89	1.87	1.86	1.84	1.79	1.76	1.74	1.71	1.69	1.66	1.65	1.61
25	1.84	1.82	1.80	1.79	1.77	1.72	1.68	1.66	1.63	1.61	1.58	1.56	1.52
30	1.79	1.77	1.75	1.74	1.72	1.67	1.63	1.61	1.57	1.55	1.52	1.51	1.46
35	1.76	1.74	1.72	1.70	1.69	1.63	1.60	1.57	1.53	1.51	1.48	1.47	1.41
40	1.74	1.71	1.70	1.68	1.66	1.61	1.57	1.54	1.51	1.48	1.45	1.43	1.38
45	1.72	1.70	1.68	1.66	1.64	1.58	1.55	1.52	1.48	1.46	1.43	1.41	1.35
50	1.70	1.68	1.66	1.64	1.63	1.57	1.53	1.50	1.46	1.44	1.41	1.39	1.33

continued

continued

dfd	dfn												
	11	12	13	14	15	20	25	30	40	50	75	100	∞
60	1.68	1.66	1.64	1.62	1.60	1.54	1.50	1.48	1.44	1.41	1.38	1.36	1.29
70	1.66	1.64	1.62	1.60	1.59	1.53	1.49	1.46	1.42	1.39	1.36	1.34	1.27
80	1.65	1.63	1.61	1.59	1.57	1.51	1.47	1.44	1.40	1.38	1.34	1.32	1.24
90	1.64	1.62	1.60	1.58	1.56	1.50	1.46	1.43	1.39	1.36	1.33	1.30	1.23
100	1.64	1.61	1.59	1.57	1.56	1.49	1.45	1.42	1.38	1.35	1.32	1.29	1.21
150	1.61	1.59	1.57	1.55	1.53	1.47	1.43	1.40	1.35	1.33	1.28	1.26	1.17
200	1.60	1.58	1.56	1.54	1.52	1.46	1.41	1.38	1.34	1.31	1.27	1.24	1.14
500	1.58	1.56	1.54	1.52	1.50	1.44	1.39	1.36	1.31	1.28	1.24	1.21	1.09
1000	1.58	1.55	1.53	1.51	1.49	1.43	1.38	1.35	1.30	1.27	1.23	1.20	1.06
∞	1.57	1.55	1.52	1.50	1.49	1.42	1.38	1.34	1.30	1.26	1.21	1.18	1.00

Table 3C Critical values of the *F* distribution with numerator and denominator degrees of freedom for α = .05.

For a given numerator and denominator degrees of freedom, this table gives the critical value of the F distribution so that the proportion of the curve to the right of that critical value is α.

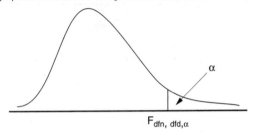

$$F_{dfn, \ dfd, \alpha}$$

					dfn					
dfd	**1**	**2**	**3**	**4**	**5**	**6**	**7**	**8**	**9**	**10**
1	161.45	199.50	215.71	224.58	230.16	233.99	236.77	238.88	240.54	241.88
2	18.51	19.00	19.16	19.25	19.30	19.33	19.35	19.37	19.38	19.40
3	10.13	9.55	9.28	9.12	9.01	8.94	8.89	8.85	8.81	8.79
4	7.71	6.94	6.59	6.39	6.26	6.16	6.09	6.04	6.00	5.96
5	6.61	5.79	5.41	5.19	5.05	4.95	4.88	4.82	4.77	4.74
6	5.99	5.14	4.76	4.53	4.39	4.28	4.21	4.15	4.10	4.06
7	5.59	4.74	4.35	4.12	3.97	3.87	3.79	3.73	3.68	3.64
8	5.32	4.46	4.07	3.84	3.69	3.58	3.50	3.44	3.39	3.35
9	5.12	4.26	3.86	3.63	3.48	3.37	3.29	3.23	3.18	3.14
10	4.97	4.10	3.71	3.48	3.33	3.22	3.14	3.07	3.02	2.98
11	4.84	3.98	3.59	3.36	3.20	3.09	3.01	2.95	2.90	2.85
12	4.75	3.89	3.49	3.26	3.11	3.00	2.91	2.85	2.80	2.75
13	4.67	3.81	3.41	3.18	3.03	2.92	2.83	2.77	2.71	2.67
14	4.60	3.74	3.34	3.11	2.96	2.85	2.76	2.70	2.65	2.60
15	4.54	3.68	3.29	3.06	2.90	2.79	2.71	2.64	2.59	2.54
16	4.49	3.63	3.24	3.01	2.85	2.74	2.66	2.59	2.54	2.49
17	4.45	3.59	3.20	2.96	2.81	2.70	2.61	2.55	2.49	2.45
18	4.41	3.55	3.16	2.93	2.77	2.66	2.58	2.51	2.46	2.41
19	4.38	3.52	3.13	2.90	2.74	2.63	2.54	2.48	2.42	2.38
20	4.35	3.49	3.10	2.87	2.71	2.60	2.51	2.45	2.39	2.35
25	4.24	3.39	2.99	2.76	2.60	2.49	2.40	2.34	2.28	2.24
30	4.17	3.32	2.92	2.69	2.53	2.42	2.33	2.27	2.21	2.16
35	4.12	3.27	2.87	2.64	2.49	2.37	2.29	2.22	2.16	2.11
40	4.09	3.23	2.84	2.61	2.45	2.34	2.25	2.18	2.12	2.08
45	4.06	3.20	2.81	2.58	2.42	2.31	2.22	2.15	2.10	2.05
50	4.03	3.18	2.79	2.56	2.40	2.29	2.20	2.13	2.07	2.03

continued

continued

dfd	dfn									
	1	2	3	4	5	6	7	8	9	10
60	4.00	3.15	2.76	2.53	2.37	2.25	2.17	2.10	2.04	1.99
70	3.98	3.13	2.74	2.50	2.35	2.23	2.14	2.07	2.02	1.97
80	3.96	3.11	2.72	2.49	2.33	2.21	2.13	2.06	2.00	1.95
90	3.95	3.10	2.71	2.47	2.32	2.20	2.11	2.04	1.99	1.94
100	3.94	3.09	2.70	2.46	2.31	2.19	2.10	2.03	1.97	1.93
150	3.90	3.06	2.66	2.43	2.27	2.16	2.07	2.00	1.94	1.89
200	3.89	3.04	2.65	2.42	2.26	2.14	2.06	1.98	1.93	1.88
500	3.86	3.01	2.62	2.39	2.23	2.12	2.03	1.96	1.90	1.85
1000	3.85	3.00	2.61	2.38	2.22	2.11	2.02	1.95	1.89	1.84
∞	3.84	3.00	2.60	2.37	2.21	2.10	2.01	1.94	1.88	1.83

Table 3D   Critical values of the *F* distribution with numerator and denominator degrees of freedom for α = .05.

For a given numerator and denominator degrees of freedom, this table gives the critical value of the F distribution so that the proportion of the curve to the right of that critical value is α.

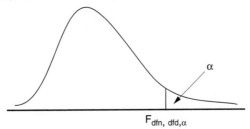

$$F_{dfn,\ dfd,\alpha}$$

dfd	11	12	13	14	15	20	25	30	40	50	75	100	∞
1	242.98	243.91	244.69	245.36	245.95	248.01	249.26	250.10	251.14	251.77	252.62	253.04	254.31
2	19.40	19.41	19.42	19.42	19.43	19.45	19.46	19.46	19.47	19.48	19.48	19.49	19.50
3	8.76	8.74	8.73	8.71	8.70	8.66	8.63	8.62	8.59	8.58	8.56	8.55	8.53
4	5.94	5.91	5.89	5.87	5.86	5.80	5.77	5.75	5.72	5.70	5.68	5.66	5.63
5	4.70	4.68	4.66	4.64	4.62	4.56	4.52	4.50	4.46	4.44	4.42	4.41	4.37
6	4.03	4.00	3.98	3.96	3.94	3.87	3.83	3.81	3.77	3.75	3.73	3.71	3.67
7	3.60	3.57	3.55	3.53	3.51	3.44	3.40	3.38	3.34	3.32	3.29	3.27	3.23
8	3.31	3.28	3.26	3.24	3.22	3.15	3.11	3.08	3.04	3.02	2.99	2.97	2.93
9	3.10	3.07	3.05	3.03	3.01	2.94	2.89	2.86	2.83	2.80	2.77	2.76	2.71
10	2.94	2.91	2.89	2.86	2.85	2.77	2.73	2.70	2.66	2.64	2.60	2.59	2.54
11	2.82	2.79	2.76	2.74	2.72	2.65	2.60	2.57	2.53	2.51	2.47	2.46	2.40
12	2.72	2.69	2.66	2.64	2.62	2.54	2.50	2.47	2.43	2.40	2.37	2.35	2.30
13	2.63	2.60	2.58	2.55	2.53	2.46	2.41	2.38	2.34	2.31	2.28	2.26	2.21
14	2.57	2.53	2.51	2.48	2.46	2.39	2.34	2.31	2.27	2.24	2.21	2.19	2.13
15	2.51	2.48	2.45	2.42	2.40	2.33	2.28	2.25	2.20	2.18	2.14	2.12	2.07
16	2.46	2.42	2.40	2.37	2.35	2.28	2.23	2.19	2.15	2.12	2.09	2.07	2.01
17	2.41	2.38	2.35	2.33	2.31	2.23	2.18	2.15	2.10	2.08	2.04	2.02	1.96
18	2.37	2.34	2.31	2.29	2.27	2.19	2.14	2.11	2.06	2.04	2.00	1.98	1.92
19	2.34	2.31	2.28	2.26	2.23	2.16	2.11	2.07	2.03	2.00	1.96	1.94	1.88
20	2.31	2.28	2.25	2.22	2.20	2.12	2.07	2.04	1.99	1.97	1.93	1.91	1.84
25	2.20	2.16	2.14	2.11	2.09	2.01	1.96	1.92	1.87	1.84	1.80	1.78	1.71
30	2.13	2.09	2.06	2.04	2.01	1.93	1.88	1.84	1.79	1.76	1.72	1.70	1.62
35	2.07	2.04	2.01	1.99	1.96	1.88	1.82	1.79	1.74	1.70	1.66	1.63	1.56
40	2.04	2.00	1.97	1.95	1.92	1.84	1.78	1.74	1.69	1.66	1.61	1.59	1.51
45	2.01	1.97	1.94	1.92	1.89	1.81	1.75	1.71	1.66	1.63	1.58	1.55	1.47
50	1.99	1.95	1.92	1.89	1.87	1.78	1.73	1.69	1.63	1.60	1.55	1.52	1.44

continued

continued

dfd	\multicolumn{13}{c}{dfn}
	11	12	13	14	15	20	25	30	40	50	75	100	∞
60	1.95	1.92	1.89	1.86	1.84	1.75	1.69	1.65	1.59	1.56	1.51	1.48	1.39
70	1.93	1.89	1.86	1.84	1.81	1.72	1.66	1.62	1.57	1.53	1.48	1.45	1.35
80	1.91	1.88	1.84	1.82	1.79	1.70	1.64	1.60	1.54	1.51	1.45	1.43	1.32
90	1.90	1.86	1.83	1.80	1.78	1.69	1.63	1.59	1.53	1.49	1.44	1.41	1.30
100	1.89	1.85	1.82	1.79	1.77	1.68	1.62	1.57	1.52	1.48	1.42	1.39	1.28
150	1.85	1.82	1.79	1.76	1.73	1.64	1.58	1.54	1.48	1.44	1.38	1.34	1.22
200	1.84	1.80	1.77	1.74	1.72	1.62	1.56	1.52	1.46	1.41	1.35	1.32	1.19
500	1.81	1.77	1.74	1.71	1.69	1.59	1.53	1.48	1.42	1.38	1.31	1.28	1.11
1000	1.80	1.76	1.73	1.70	1.68	1.58	1.52	1.47	1.41	1.36	1.30	1.26	1.08
∞	1.79	1.75	1.72	1.69	1.67	1.57	1.51	1.46	1.39	1.35	1.28	1.24	1.00

Table 3E   Critical values of the *F* distribution with numerator and denominator degrees of freedom for $\alpha = .025$.

For a given numerator and denominator degrees of freedom, this table gives the critical value of the F distribution so that the proportion of the curve to the right of that critical value is α.

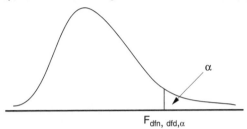

$$F_{dfn,\ dfd,\alpha}$$

dfd	dfn									
	1	2	3	4	5	6	7	8	9	10
1	647.79	799.50	864.16	899.58	921.85	937.11	948.22	956.66	963.28	968.63
2	38.51	39.00	39.17	39.25	39.30	39.33	39.36	39.37	39.39	39.40
3	17.44	16.04	15.44	15.10	14.88	14.73	14.62	14.54	14.47	14.42
4	12.22	10.65	9.98	9.60	9.36	9.20	9.07	8.98	8.90	8.84
5	10.01	8.43	7.76	7.39	7.15	6.98	6.85	6.76	6.68	6.62
6	8.81	7.26	6.60	6.23	5.99	5.82	5.70	5.60	5.52	5.46
7	8.07	6.54	5.89	5.52	5.29	5.12	4.99	4.90	4.82	4.76
8	7.57	6.06	5.42	5.05	4.82	4.65	4.53	4.43	4.36	4.30
9	7.21	5.71	5.08	4.72	4.48	4.32	4.20	4.10	4.03	3.96
10	6.94	5.46	4.83	4.47	4.24	4.07	3.95	3.85	3.78	3.72
11	6.72	5.26	4.63	4.28	4.04	3.88	3.76	3.66	3.59	3.53
12	6.55	5.10	4.47	4.12	3.89	3.73	3.61	3.51	3.44	3.37
13	6.41	4.97	4.35	4.00	3.77	3.60	3.48	3.39	3.31	3.25
14	6.30	4.86	4.24	3.89	3.66	3.50	3.38	3.29	3.21	3.15
15	6.20	4.77	4.15	3.80	3.58	3.41	3.29	3.20	3.12	3.06
16	6.12	4.69	4.08	3.73	3.50	3.34	3.22	3.12	3.05	2.99
17	6.04	4.62	4.01	3.66	3.44	3.28	3.16	3.06	2.98	2.92
18	5.98	4.56	3.95	3.61	3.38	3.22	3.10	3.01	2.93	2.87
19	5.92	4.51	3.90	3.56	3.33	3.17	3.05	2.96	2.88	2.82
20	5.87	4.46	3.86	3.51	3.29	3.13	3.01	2.91	2.84	2.77
25	5.69	4.29	3.69	3.35	3.13	2.97	2.85	2.75	2.68	2.61
30	5.57	4.18	3.59	3.25	3.03	2.87	2.75	2.65	2.57	2.51
35	5.49	4.11	3.52	3.18	2.96	2.80	2.68	2.58	2.50	2.44
40	5.42	4.05	3.46	3.13	2.90	2.74	2.62	2.53	2.45	2.39
45	5.38	4.01	3.42	3.09	2.86	2.70	2.58	2.49	2.41	2.35
50	5.34	3.97	3.39	3.05	2.83	2.67	2.55	2.46	2.38	2.32

continued

Statistical Tables

continued

| dfd | \multicolumn{10}{c}{dfn} |
---	1	2	3	4	5	6	7	8	9	10
60	5.29	3.93	3.34	3.01	2.79	2.63	2.51	2.41	2.33	2.27
70	5.25	3.89	3.31	2.97	2.75	2.59	2.47	2.38	2.30	2.24
80	5.22	3.86	3.28	2.95	2.73	2.57	2.45	2.35	2.28	2.21
90	5.20	3.84	3.26	2.93	2.71	2.55	2.43	2.34	2.26	2.19
100	5.18	3.83	3.25	2.92	2.70	2.54	2.42	2.32	2.24	2.18
150	5.13	3.78	3.20	2.87	2.65	2.49	2.37	2.28	2.20	2.13
200	5.10	3.76	3.18	2.85	2.63	2.47	2.35	2.26	2.18	2.11
500	5.05	3.72	3.14	2.81	2.59	2.43	2.31	2.22	2.14	2.07
1000	5.04	3.70	3.13	2.80	2.58	2.42	2.30	2.20	2.13	2.06
∞	5.02	3.69	3.12	2.79	2.57	2.41	2.29	2.19	2.11	2.05

Table 3F Critical values of the *F* distribution with numerator and denominator degrees of freedom for α = .025.

For a given numerator and denominator degrees of freedom, this table gives the critical value of the F distribution so that the proportion of the curve to the right of that critical value is α.

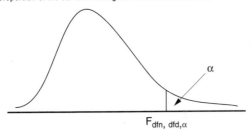

$F_{dfn, \ dfd, \alpha}$

dfd						dfn							
	11	12	13	14	15	20	25	30	40	50	75	100	∞
1	973.03	976.71	979.84	982.53	984.87	993.10	998.08	1001.41	1005.60	1008.12	1011.49	1013.17	1018.26
2	39.41	39.41	39.42	39.43	39.43	39.45	39.46	39.46	39.47	39.48	39.48	39.49	39.50
3	14.37	14.34	14.30	14.28	14.25	14.17	14.12	14.08	14.04	14.01	13.97	13.96	13.90
4	8.79	8.75	8.71	8.68	8.66	8.56	8.50	8.46	8.41	8.38	8.34	8.32	8.26
5	6.57	6.52	6.49	6.46	6.43	6.33	6.27	6.23	6.18	6.14	6.10	6.08	6.02
6	5.41	5.37	5.33	5.30	5.27	5.17	5.11	5.07	5.01	4.98	4.94	4.92	4.85
7	4.71	4.67	4.63	4.60	4.57	4.47	4.40	4.36	4.31	4.28	4.23	4.21	4.14
8	4.24	4.20	4.16	4.13	4.10	4.00	3.94	3.89	3.84	3.81	3.76	3.74	3.67
9	3.91	3.87	3.83	3.80	3.77	3.67	3.60	3.56	3.51	3.47	3.43	3.40	3.33
10	3.66	3.62	3.58	3.55	3.52	3.42	3.35	3.31	3.26	3.22	3.18	3.15	3.08
11	3.47	3.43	3.39	3.36	3.33	3.23	3.16	3.12	3.06	3.03	2.98	2.96	2.88
12	3.32	3.28	3.24	3.21	3.18	3.07	3.01	2.96	2.91	2.87	2.82	2.80	2.72
13	3.20	3.15	3.12	3.08	3.05	2.95	2.88	2.84	2.78	2.74	2.70	2.67	2.60
14	3.09	3.05	3.01	2.98	2.95	2.84	2.78	2.73	2.67	2.64	2.59	2.56	2.49
15	3.01	2.96	2.92	2.89	2.86	2.76	2.69	2.64	2.59	2.55	2.50	2.47	2.40
16	2.93	2.89	2.85	2.82	2.79	2.68	2.61	2.57	2.51	2.47	2.42	2.40	2.32
17	2.87	2.82	2.79	2.75	2.72	2.62	2.55	2.50	2.44	2.41	2.35	2.33	2.25
18	2.81	2.77	2.73	2.70	2.67	2.56	2.49	2.44	2.38	2.35	2.30	2.27	2.19
19	2.76	2.72	2.68	2.65	2.62	2.51	2.44	2.39	2.33	2.30	2.24	2.22	2.13
20	2.72	2.68	2.64	2.60	2.57	2.46	2.40	2.35	2.29	2.25	2.20	2.17	2.09
25	2.56	2.51	2.48	2.44	2.41	2.30	2.23	2.18	2.12	2.08	2.02	2.00	1.91
30	2.46	2.41	2.37	2.34	2.31	2.20	2.12	2.07	2.01	1.97	1.91	1.88	1.79
35	2.39	2.34	2.30	2.27	2.23	2.12	2.05	2.00	1.93	1.89	1.83	1.80	1.70
40	2.33	2.29	2.25	2.21	2.18	2.07	1.99	1.94	1.88	1.83	1.77	1.74	1.64
45	2.29	2.25	2.21	2.17	2.14	2.03	1.95	1.90	1.83	1.79	1.73	1.69	1.59
50	2.26	2.22	2.18	2.14	2.11	1.99	1.92	1.87	1.80	1.75	1.69	1.66	1.55

continued

continued

dfd	11	12	13	14	15	20	25	30	40	50	75	100	∞
						dfn							
60	2.22	2.17	2.13	2.09	2.06	1.94	1.87	1.82	1.74	1.70	1.63	1.60	1.48
70	2.18	2.14	2.10	2.06	2.03	1.91	1.83	1.78	1.71	1.66	1.59	1.56	1.44
80	2.16	2.11	2.07	2.03	2.00	1.88	1.81	1.75	1.68	1.63	1.56	1.53	1.40
90	2.14	2.09	2.05	2.02	1.98	1.86	1.79	1.73	1.66	1.61	1.54	1.50	1.37
100	2.12	2.08	2.04	2.00	1.97	1.85	1.77	1.71	1.64	1.59	1.52	1.48	1.35
150	2.08	2.03	1.99	1.95	1.92	1.80	1.72	1.67	1.59	1.54	1.46	1.42	1.27
200	2.06	2.01	1.97	1.93	1.90	1.78	1.70	1.64	1.56	1.51	1.44	1.39	1.23
500	2.02	1.97	1.93	1.89	1.86	1.74	1.65	1.60	1.52	1.46	1.38	1.34	1.14
1000	2.01	1.96	1.92	1.88	1.85	1.72	1.64	1.58	1.50	1.45	1.36	1.32	1.09
∞	1.99	1.94	1.90	1.87	1.83	1.71	1.63	1.57	1.48	1.43	1.34	1.30	1.00

Table 3G Critical values of the *F* distribution with numerator and denominator degrees of freedom for α = .01.

For a given numerator and denominator degrees of freedom, this table gives the critical value of the F distribution so that the proportion of the curve to the right of that critical value is α.

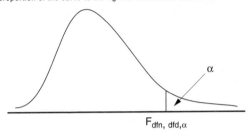

$F_{dfn, \ dfd, \alpha}$

					dfn					
dfd	**1**	**2**	**3**	**4**	**5**	**6**	**7**	**8**	**9**	**10**
1	4052	5000	5403	5625	5764	5859	5928	5981	6022	6056
2	98.50	99.00	99.17	99.25	99.30	99.33	99.36	99.37	99.39	99.40
3	34.12	30.82	29.46	28.71	28.24	27.91	27.67	27.49	27.35	27.23
4	21.20	18.00	16.69	15.98	15.52	15.21	14.98	14.80	14.66	14.55
5	16.26	13.27	12.06	11.39	10.97	10.67	10.46	10.29	10.16	10.05
6	13.75	10.92	9.78	9.15	8.75	8.47	8.26	8.10	7.98	7.87
7	12.25	9.55	8.45	7.85	7.46	7.19	6.99	6.84	6.72	6.62
8	11.26	8.65	7.59	7.01	6.63	6.37	6.18	6.03	5.91	5.81
9	10.56	8.02	6.99	6.42	6.06	5.80	5.61	5.47	5.35	5.26
10	10.04	7.56	6.55	5.99	5.64	5.39	5.20	5.06	4.94	4.85
11	9.65	7.21	6.22	5.67	5.32	5.07	4.89	4.74	4.63	4.54
12	9.33	6.93	5.95	5.41	5.06	4.82	4.64	4.50	4.39	4.30
13	9.07	6.70	5.74	5.21	4.86	4.62	4.44	4.30	4.19	4.10
14	8.86	6.51	5.56	5.04	4.69	4.46	4.28	4.14	4.03	3.94
15	8.68	6.36	5.42	4.89	4.56	4.32	4.14	4.00	3.89	3.80
16	8.53	6.23	5.29	4.77	4.44	4.20	4.03	3.89	3.78	3.69
17	8.40	6.11	5.18	4.67	4.34	4.10	3.93	3.79	3.68	3.59
18	8.29	6.01	5.09	4.58	4.25	4.01	3.84	3.71	3.60	3.51
19	8.18	5.93	5.01	4.50	4.17	3.94	3.77	3.63	3.52	3.43
20	8.10	5.85	4.94	4.43	4.10	3.87	3.70	3.56	3.46	3.37
25	7.77	5.57	4.68	4.18	3.85	3.63	3.46	3.32	3.22	3.13
30	7.56	5.39	4.51	4.02	3.70	3.47	3.30	3.17	3.07	2.98
35	7.42	5.27	4.40	3.91	3.59	3.37	3.20	3.07	2.96	2.88
40	7.31	5.18	4.31	3.83	3.51	3.29	3.12	2.99	2.89	2.80
45	7.23	5.11	4.25	3.77	3.45	3.23	3.07	2.94	2.83	2.74
50	7.17	5.06	4.20	3.72	3.41	3.19	3.02	2.89	2.78	2.70

continued

continued

dfd	dfn									
	1	2	3	4	5	6	7	8	9	10
60	7.08	4.98	4.13	3.65	3.34	3.12	2.95	2.82	2.72	2.63
70	7.01	4.92	4.07	3.60	3.29	3.07	2.91	2.78	2.67	2.59
80	6.96	4.88	4.04	3.56	3.26	3.04	2.87	2.74	2.64	2.55
90	6.93	4.85	4.01	3.53	3.23	3.01	2.84	2.72	2.61	2.52
100	6.90	4.82	3.98	3.51	3.21	2.99	2.82	2.69	2.59	2.50
150	6.81	4.75	3.91	3.45	3.14	2.92	2.76	2.63	2.53	2.44
200	6.76	4.71	3.88	3.41	3.11	2.89	2.73	2.60	2.50	2.41
500	6.69	4.65	3.82	3.36	3.05	2.84	2.68	2.55	2.44	2.36
1000	6.66	4.63	3.80	3.34	3.04	2.82	2.66	2.53	2.43	2.34
∞	6.63	4.61	3.78	3.32	3.02	2.80	2.64	2.51	2.41	2.32

Table 4 Critical values of the chi-squared distribution with degrees of freedom = v.

For a given degrees of freedom, the critical value of the chi-squared distribution is listed for each value of α, where α is the proportion of total area under the curve to the left of the critical value. So $1 - \alpha$ is the area to the right of the critical value.

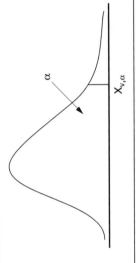

$X_{v,\alpha}$

v	0.001	0.005	0.010	0.025	0.050	0.100	0.500	0.900	0.950	0.975	0.990	0.995	0.999
1	0.000	0.000	0.000	0.001	0.004	0.016	0.455	2.706	3.841	5.024	6.635	7.879	10.828
2	0.002	0.010	0.020	0.051	0.103	0.211	1.386	4.605	5.991	7.378	9.210	10.597	13.816
3	0.024	0.072	0.115	0.216	0.352	0.584	2.366	6.251	7.815	9.348	11.345	12.838	16.266
4	0.091	0.207	0.297	0.484	0.711	1.064	3.357	7.779	9.488	11.143	13.277	14.860	18.467
5	0.210	0.412	0.554	0.831	1.145	1.610	4.351	9.236	11.070	12.833	15.086	16.750	20.515
6	0.381	0.676	0.872	1.237	1.635	2.204	5.348	10.645	12.592	14.449	16.812	18.548	22.458
7	0.598	0.989	1.239	1.690	2.167	2.833	6.346	12.017	14.067	16.013	18.475	20.278	24.322
8	0.857	1.344	1.646	2.180	2.733	3.490	7.344	13.362	15.507	17.535	20.090	21.955	26.124
9	1.152	1.735	2.088	2.700	3.325	4.168	8.343	14.684	16.919	19.023	21.666	23.589	27.877
10	1.479	2.156	2.558	3.247	3.940	4.865	9.342	15.987	18.307	20.483	23.209	25.188	29.588

continued

continued

ν	\(\alpha\)												
	0.001	0.005	0.010	0.025	0.050	0.100	0.500	0.900	0.950	0.975	0.990	0.995	0.999
11	1.834	2.603	3.053	3.816	4.575	5.578	10.341	17.275	19.675	21.920	24.725	26.757	31.264
12	2.214	3.074	3.571	4.404	5.226	6.304	11.340	18.549	21.026	23.337	26.217	28.300	32.909
13	2.617	3.565	4.107	5.009	5.892	7.042	12.340	19.812	22.362	24.736	27.688	29.819	34.528
14	3.041	4.075	4.660	5.629	6.571	7.790	13.339	21.064	23.685	26.119	29.141	31.319	36.123
15	3.483	4.601	5.229	6.262	7.261	8.547	14.339	22.307	24.996	27.488	30.578	32.801	37.697
16	3.942	5.142	5.812	6.908	7.962	9.312	15.338	23.542	26.296	28.845	32.000	34.267	39.252
17	4.416	5.697	6.408	7.564	8.672	10.085	16.338	24.769	27.587	30.191	33.409	35.718	40.790
18	4.905	6.265	7.015	8.231	9.390	10.865	17.338	25.989	28.869	31.526	34.805	37.156	42.312
19	5.407	6.844	7.633	8.907	10.117	11.651	18.338	27.204	30.144	32.852	36.191	38.582	43.820
20	5.921	7.434	8.260	9.591	10.851	12.443	19.337	28.412	31.410	34.170	37.566	39.997	45.315
25	8.649	10.520	11.524	13.120	14.611	16.473	24.337	34.382	37.652	40.646	44.314	46.928	52.620
30	11.588	13.787	14.953	16.791	18.493	20.599	29.336	40.256	43.773	46.979	50.892	53.672	59.703
35	14.688	17.192	18.509	20.569	22.465	24.797	34.336	46.059	49.802	53.203	57.342	60.275	66.619
40	17.916	20.707	22.164	24.433	26.509	29.051	39.335	51.805	55.758	59.342	63.691	66.766	73.402
50	24.674	27.991	29.707	32.357	34.764	37.689	49.335	63.167	67.505	71.420	76.154	79.490	86.661
60	31.738	35.534	37.485	40.482	43.188	46.459	59.335	74.397	79.082	83.298	88.379	91.952	99.607
70	39.036	43.275	45.442	48.758	51.739	55.329	69.334	85.527	90.531	95.023	100.425	104.215	112.317
80	46.520	51.172	53.540	57.153	60.391	64.278	79.334	96.578	101.879	106.629	112.329	116.321	124.839
90	54.155	59.196	61.754	65.647	69.126	73.291	89.334	107.565	113.145	118.136	124.116	128.299	137.208
100	61.918	67.328	70.065	74.222	77.929	82.358	99.334	118.498	124.342	129.561	135.807	140.169	149.449

Table 5 Factors for control charts.

Obs n	Chart for Averages			Chart for Standard Deviations						Chart for Ranges						
	Factors for Control Limits			Factors for Central Line		Factors for Control Limits				Factors for Central Line			Factors for Control Limits			
	A	A_2	A_3	c_4	$1/c_4$	B_3	B_4	B_5	B_6	d_2	$1/d_2$	d_3	D_1	D_2	D_3	D_4
2	2.121	1.881	2.659	0.7979	1.2533	0	3.267	0	2.606	1.128	0.8865	0.853	0	3.686	0	3.267
3	1.732	1.023	1.954	0.8862	1.1284	0	2.568	0	2.276	1.693	0.5907	0.888	0	4.358	0	2.575
4	1.500	0.729	1.628	0.9213	1.0854	0	2.266	0	2.088	2.059	0.4857	0.880	0	4.698	0	2.282
5	1.342	0.577	1.427	0.9400	1.0638	0	2.089	0	1.964	2.326	0.4299	0.864	0	4.918	0	2.114
6	1.225	0.483	1.287	0.9515	1.0509	0.030	1.970	0.029	1.874	2.534	0.3946	0.848	0	5.079	0	2.004
7	1.134	0.419	1.182	0.9594	1.0424	0.118	1.882	0.113	1.806	2.704	0.3698	0.833	0.205	5.204	0.076	1.924
8	1.061	0.373	1.099	0.9650	1.0362	0.185	1.815	0.179	1.751	2.847	0.3512	0.820	0.388	5.307	0.136	1.864
9	1.000	0.337	1.032	0.9693	1.0317	0.239	1.761	0.232	1.707	2.970	0.3367	0.808	0.547	5.394	0.184	1.816
10	0.949	0.308	0.975	0.9727	1.0281	0.284	1.716	0.276	1.669	3.078	0.3249	0.797	0.686	5.469	0.223	1.777
11	0.905	0.285	0.927	0.9754	1.0253	0.321	1.679	0.313	1.637	3.173	0.3152	0.787	0.811	5.535	0.256	1.744
12	0.866	0.266	0.886	0.9776	1.0230	0.354	1.646	0.346	1.610	3.258	0.3069	0.778	0.923	5.594	0.283	1.717
13	0.832	0.249	0.850	0.9794	1.0210	0.382	1.618	0.374	1.585	3.336	0.2998	0.770				
14	0.802	0.235	0.817	0.9810	1.0194	0.406	1.594	0.399	1.563	3.407	0.2935	0.763				
15	0.775	0.223	0.789	0.9823	1.0180	0.428	1.572	0.421	1.544	3.472	0.2880	0.756				
16	0.750	0.212	0.763	0.9835	1.0168	0.448	1.552	0.440	1.526	3.532	0.2831	0.750				
17	0.728	0.203	0.739	0.9845	1.0157	0.466	1.534	0.458	1.511	3.588	0.2787	0.744				
18	0.707	0.194	0.718	0.9854	1.0148	0.482	1.518	0.475	1.496	3.640	0.2747	0.739				
19	0.688	0.187	0.698	0.9862	1.0140	0.497	1.503	0.490	1.483	3.689	0.2711	0.733				

continued

continued

	Chart for Averages			Chart for Standard Deviations							Chart for Ranges						
	Factors for Control Limits			Factors for Central Line		Factors for Control Limits				Factors for Central Line			Factors for Control Limits			
Obs																	
n	A	A_2	A_3	c_4	$1/c_4$	B_3	B_4	B_5	B_6	d_2	$1/d_2$	d_3	D_1	D_2	D_3	D_4
20	0.671	0.180	0.680	0.9869	1.0132	0.510	1.490	0.504	1.470	3.735	0.2677	0.729				
21	0.655	0.173	0.663	0.9876	1.0126	0.523	1.477	0.516	1.459	3.778	0.2647	0.724				
22	0.640	0.167	0.647	0.9882	1.0120	0.534	1.466	0.528	1.448	3.819	0.2618	0.720				
23	0.626	0.162	0.633	0.9887	1.0114	0.545	1.455	0.539	1.438	3.858	0.2592	0.716				
24	0.612	0.157	0.619	0.9892	1.0109	0.555	1.445	0.549	1.429	3.895	0.2567	0.712				
25	0.600	0.153	0.606	0.9896	1.0105	0.565	1.435	0.559	1.420	3.931	0.2544	0.708				

References

1. American Society for Quality, *Quality Glossary* (accessed 15 February 2004) www.asq.org/info/glossary.
2. ANSI/ASQ Z1.4-2003, *Sampling Procedures and Tables for Inspection by Attributes* (Milwaukee: American Society for Quality).
3. ANSI/ASQ Z1.9-2003, *Sampling Procedures and Tables for Inspection by Variables for Percent Nonconforming* (Milwaukee: American Society for Quality).
4. ANSI/ASQC A1-1978, *Definitions, Symbols, Formulas, and Tables for Control Charts* (Milwaukee: American Society for Quality Control).
5. ANSI/ASQC A2-1978, *Definitions, Symbols, Formulas, and Tables for Control Charts* (Milwaukee: American Society for Quality Control).
6. ANSI/ASQC A3-1978, *Definitions, Symbols, Formulas, and Tables for Control Charts* (Milwaukee: American Society for Quality Control).
7. ANSI/ASQC B2-1996, *Control Chart Method of Analyzing Data* (Milwaukee: American Society for Quality Control).
8. ANSI/ASQC B3-1996, *Control Chart Method of Controlling Quality During Production* (Milwaukee: American Society for Quality Control).
9. ANSI/ISO/ASQ Q9000-2000, *Quality management systems—Fundamentals and vocabulary* (Milwaukee: American Society for Quality).
10. ASQ Chemical and Process Industries Division, Chemical Interest Committee, *Trusting Measurement Results in the Chemical and Process Industries* (Milwaukee: ASQ Quality Press, 2001).
11. ASQ Chemical and Process Industries Division, Chemical Interest Committee, *Quality Assurance for the Chemical and Process Industries*, 2nd ed. (Milwaukee: ASQ Quality Press, 1999).
12. ASQ Statistics Division, *Glossary and Tables for Statistical Quality Control,* 3rd ed. (Milwaukee: ASQ Quality Press, 1996).
13. ASQC Chemical and Process Industries Division, Chemical Interest Committee, *Specifications for the Chemical and Process Industries* (Milwaukee: American Society for Quality Control, 1996).
14. ASQC Statistics Technical Committee, *Glossary and Tables for Statistical Quality Control* (Milwaukee: American Society for Quality Control, 1973).

15. ASTM E456-xx, *Terminology for Statistical Methods* (Philadelphia: American Society for Testing and Materials, 19xx).
16. Allan G. Bluman, *Elementary Statistics: A Brief Version*, 2nd ed. (New York: McGraw-Hill, 2003).
17. BSR/ISO/ASQ 3534-1.3-200X, *Statistics—Vocabulary and Symbols— Part 1: Probability and General Terms* (Milwaukee: American Society for Quality Control).
18. BSR/ISO/ASQ 3534-2-200X, *Statistics—Vocabulary and Symbols—Part 2: Applied Statistics* (Milwaukee: American Society for Quality Control).
19. BSR/ISO/ASQ 3534-3-1999, *Statistics—Vocabulary and Symbols—Part 3: Design of Experiments* (Geneva, Switzerland: International Organization for Standardization, 1999).
20. David C. Hoaglin, Frederick Mosteller, and John W. Tukey, *Understanding Robust and Exploratory Data Analysis* (New York: John Wiley & Sons, 1983).
21. J. Stuart Hunter, "The Exponentially Weighted Moving Average" *Journal of Quality Technology* 18 (1986): 203–9.
22. Frank C. Kaminsky, James C. Benneyan, Robert D. Davis, and Richard J. Burke, "Statistical Control Charts Based on a Geometric Distribution," *Journal of Quality Technology* 24, no. 2 (1992).
23. Samuel Kotz and Norman L. Johnson, "Process Capability Indices—A Review, 1992–2000" *Journal of Quality Technology* 34, no. 1 (2000): 2ff.
24. MIL-STD-721, *Definitions of Terms for Reliability and Maintainability* (Washington, DC: Department of Defense).
25. Minitab, Inc., *Minitab, Release 13* (State College, PA: Minitab, 2001).
26. Douglas C. Montgomery, *Introduction to Statistical Quality Control*, 4th ed. (New York: John Wiley & Sons, 2001).
27. Lloyd S. Nelson, "Notes on the Shewhart Control Chart," *Journal of Quality Technology* 31, no. 1 (1999).
28. NIST/SEMATECH e-Handbook of Statistical Methods http://www.itl.nist.gov/div898/handbook/, February 15, 2004.
29. Barbara F. Ryan, Brian L. Joiner, and Thomas A. Ryan, *Minitab Handbook*, 2nd ed. (Boston: Duxbury Press, 1985).
30. Team definition developed by *Glossary and Tables for Statistical Quality Control*, Fourth Edition authors.
31. John W. Tukey, *Exploratory Data Analysis* (Reading, MA: Addison-Wesley, 1977).
32. Paul F. Velleman and David C. Hoaglin, *Applications, Basics, and Computing of Exploratory Data Analysis* (Boston: Duxbury Press, 1981).
33. William H. Von Alven, ed., *Reliability Engineering* (Englewood Cliffs, NJ: Prentice-Hall, 1964).